The Evaluation Process

in HEALTH EDUCATION
PHYSICAL EDUCATION
and RECREATION

MARJORIE LATCHAW
CAMILLE BROWN

University of California
Los Angeles

The Evaluation Process
in HEALTH EDUCATION
PHYSICAL EDUCATION
and RECREATION

1962

PRENTICE-HALL, INC. Englewood Cliffs, N.J.

FOREWORD

With an increasing understanding among educators of individual differences and of the significance in the learning process of a particular individual's perception of his experience, the necessity to understand the individual's status in relation to his goals and purposes has become a central concern.

This book is a comprehensive guide to the understanding of the tools by which teachers in Health Education, Physical Education and Recreation may find individual needs in relation to individual goals and thus help students in the process of self-assessment, resetting of goals and selection of appropriate experiences for goal achievement.

Further, this book is indeed comprehensive in the philosophical framework in which evaluative tools and their use are discussed. This framework sees the healthy growth and development of the individual as the central integrating factor for the evaluative process within the three disciplines. It also shows all evaluative tools within a contemporary democratic value structure, thus forcing the evaluator to declare the values with which he is concerned.

The authors have indeed pointed new directions in the purposes and process of assessment within Health Education, Physical Education and Recreation. The chapters on assessment of individual motives and creative experiences are of particular value. The chapter on marking and grading presents a sharp and unequivocal analysis of the negative learnings achieved by present-day practices.

This book makes clear the need for a creative, individualized teaching-learning process. It provides the tools for such individualized experiences and shows the imperative need for these new directions in the education of teachers both in pre-service and in-service professional preparation in Health Education, Physical Education and Recreation.

ROSALIND CASSIDY

Department of Physical Education
University of California
Los Angeles

v

PREFACE

The focus of this book is on understanding responsible evaluation of the individual, the environments influencing him and the experiences in which he participates.

One major objective of the authors was to present evaluation procedures which could be used in actual teaching-learning situations. These are not the usual measurement instruments which can be used only by the researcher.

A second objective was to relate measurement directly to the value it was to measure. The primary value from which other values were derived is the worth and dignity of the individual within contemporary United States.

A third objective was to remember that the individual is a whole, living, breathing organism, and that he should be evaluated in his wholeness.

In an effort to satisfy these objectives, the authors have sought to organize the book somewhat differently from the customary book of this type. An attempt has been made to keep essential integration by not segmenting the individual into false strands—such as physical, mental, emotional and social—but by organizing around values inherent in healthy growth and development. We are sorry that Chapter 3 is lengthy, but we believe that the reader can see the meaning of wholeness of the individual and relationships of health education, physical education and recreation more completely if the evaluative criteria are kept intact.

Decisions had to be made in order to keep the material within the space of a single book. Accordingly, available sports skill tests and copyrighted inventories are not reprinted, but references are listed so that the student can easily obtain them. If students are to get full understandings of the evaluation process, they must actually develop and use evaluation procedures. Suggestions for student experiences have been made at the beginning of each chapter. Instructors and students will have other ideas for vitalizing the process.

We hope that this book will aid its readers to make decisions more easily on the basis of value in the work and play life of boys, girls, youth and adults.

We are indebted to our colleagues in the department of physical education, University of California, Los Angeles, realizing that many of our understandings are a composite of our experiences in working with them. We wish to express a special debt of gratitude to Dr. Rosalind Cassidy for her constant support and friendship and for reaffirming our belief in the democratic process through her work with both students and faculty.

We are indebted to the authors and publishers whose publications contributed to this book.

Special appreciation is extended to our friend, Rue Wise, Fine Art Studio, Hermosa Beach, California who graciously contributed the drawings.

MARJORIE LATCHAW
CAMILLE BROWN

CONTENTS

ix

PART FOUR
Finding Out About the Experiences

PART ONE

Finding out about THE EVALUATION PROCESS

Competencies Needed by Teachers and Leaders in Health Education, Physical Education and Recreation

1. To understand the need for evaluation in health education, physical education and recreation

2. To understand the evaluation process in health education, physical education and recreation

Competency	Value or Criterion
To understand the need for evaluation in health education, physical education and recreation	The program in health education, physical education and recreation in contemporary United States
To understand the evaluation process in health education, physical education and recreation	Healthy growth and development of the individual in contemporary United States

1

NEED FOR EVALUATION

EVALUATION COMPETENCIES

To understand:
1. *the function of evaluation in health education*
2. *the function of evaluation in physical education*
3. *the function of evaluation in recreation*

EXPERIENCES FOR THE STUDENT

1. *Discuss "healthy growth and development" as the goal of health education, of physical education, of recreation.*
2. *Discuss the relationship of "fitness" to healthy growth and development of the individual.*
3. *Discuss the similarities and differences among the contributions of the three fields to the healthy growth and development of the individual.*

In the fields of health education, physical education and recreation many changes are occurring. Changes are natural within these fields since they are based upon scientific foundations concerned with the sciences of individuals, their relationships with each other and the world in which they live. As advances occur in these sciences, the fields of health education, physical education and recreation take on new importance and must be seen in new lights.

Teachers and leaders in health education, physical education and recreation must be aware of these changing values and must help individuals chart courses to live best within their own particular cultures.

Leaders in these fields would agree that the individual is central, and that their work is directed toward helping the individual achieve his potentialities, achieve healthy growth and development. An examination of the function of evaluation in each of these three fields indicates the use of many of the same evaluation techniques if the accepted goal of each of the fields is individual achievement of healthy growth and development. In this book, the concept, "achieving potentialities," is

3

included in the concept "achieving healthy growth and development," and is accepted as the primary goal of health education, physical education and recreation.

Separate courses in the evaluation of health education, of physical education, of recreation result in proliferation of content. Teachers and leaders in all three fields should know how to evaluate individual status, practices and motives in order to help the individual achieve healthy growth and development. They should know how to appraise environments for which they are responsible. They should be competent in evaluating the worth of the experiences they provide and the value of the programs to the individual participant. The experiences in the three fields differ, but the processes for evaluating the experiences are one and the same.

Function of Evaluation in Health Education

Traditionally, the field of health education has been defined to include the areas of health services, healthful school living and health instruction. Teachers and leaders in health education are usually employed within the public schools and colleges as either health coordinators, health counselors or health teachers. Such teachers and leaders are concerned for and have responsibilities within the areas of health services, healthful school living and health instruction. They should be able to understand evaluation in each of these areas since it relates to the healthy growth and development of the individual.

The health coordinator, counselor or teacher must understand the meaning of healthy growth and development. He should be able to define the materials and conditions necessary for health. He should be able to understand the developing organism within a particular culture. The whole individual and his state of being is the concern of the health educator. The health educator is focused upon helping each individual achieve his own best health. To do this, the health educator has a real need to fully understand the evaluation process.

The health educator's use of evaluation. The health educator should be able to determine the individual's health status. He should be able to use health service records and reports, and he should be able to identify the experiences within his control which will favorably affect the individual's health. He does this by providing particular experiences in health instruction, assistance in following through with health service diagnosis and by improving the conditions of healthful school living. The health education personnel are closely related to other members of the school and community who are responsible for the health of the child. Evaluation becomes a group responsibility in identifying and alleviating health problems.

The educational preparation of the health educator defines his responsibility in a school's evaluation program. If he is a medical doctor, he assumes health diagnosis responsibilities. If he is a trained psychometrist, he administers certain tests which a teacher is unable to administer. If he is a special health educator—a teacher of "health"—he assumes the responsibilities of health instruction and health coordination. The health teacher's particular responsibility is in helping children and youth understand their own health status so that a diagnosed health need is accepted by the individual as his *own* health problem which he must solve. This is, perhaps, the greatest responsibility of the health teacher.

A leader in health education may be given the responsibility of evaluating the total health service program, the healthful school living and the health instruction program of a school or community. Such evaluation is essential to the proper growth and development of individuals within the school and the community.

All health education personnel should know how to assess individual status, practices and motives in order to better understand the individual's health needs. They should be able to assess the environments and the experiences. They should know how to appraise health education programs in school and community.

The health educator, however, does not assume this responsibility alone. The physical education teacher and the recreation leader are also vitally concerned with the health of the individual. Program development in all of these fields begins with understanding the individual so that experiences may be provided which are appropriate to him. Many teachers and leaders call this initial understanding of the individual "health education." Having identified the individual's concerns, the physical education teacher and recreation leader attempt to provide the experiences within their particular fields which will help him achieve his goals. The physical education teacher and the recreation leader are also concerned about the healthful environment and should know how to evaluate within their particular situations so that they can provide such an environment.

Physical education and recreation, broadly conceived, may be considered a part of "health education." Health education, however, includes *more* than is encompassed in physical education and recreation. Health education is concerned with every aspect of the nature of the individual in his world.

Function of Evaluation in Physical Education

Basically, physical education is human movement directed toward the successful management of the human organism. Management of the human organism means the combined processes of *being* and *doing*. The person becomes something while doing something. Just as the word "movement" itself describes the interaction of the individual and the environment, so does the word "management." It signifies that the individual has the "power to act" and does "act." His act may be creative, re-creative, educative or re-educative, task oriented or coping-with-the-environment oriented. The act or the movement contributes to the healthy growth and development of the organism.

The physical education teacher's use of evaluation.   The physical education teacher works directly with the individual in helping him learn how to manage his changing body within his changing environments throughout his life span. The teacher's role is one of identifying where the individual is in relation to this task and of assisting him in what can best be learned at his particular stage of growth and development.

Since the real concerns of a child at any one time must be related to his experiences, evaluation tools must be used by the teacher for the selection of experiences which meet the real needs of a particular child in his own stage of development. These tools must provide information about the individual's status, practices and motives, and the selected experiences should be evaluated in light of individual needs. The physical education teacher should also evaluate the environments of the individual, and he should know how to assess the physical education program.

All of physical education is a part of health education. School physical education, however, is not recreation, although a purpose of physical education leaders may be to prepare people to have certain recreational skills and abilities and to foster an urge for active participation in gross movement experiences during leisure. Thus, gross movement experiences may be thought of as recreational skills which are taught in physical education.

The physical education teacher may be prepared to work within a community recreation program. Numerous recreation programs provide physical education experiences for both children and adults.

All physical education is not re-creative in nature. Some of it may be for some individuals. The development of a desire for and love of moving contributes greatly to the recreational appetite. The preparation of the individual in successful management of his body will lead toward meeting recreational goals.

Function of Evaluation in Recreation

Recreation is considered to be the re-creative experiences in which individuals voluntarily participate during their leisure time. An individual's re-creative experiences may be of any nature, such as reading, thinking, creating, associating. These may be the same experiences which within the school program are called "education." They may be health education experiences, physical education experiences or educational experiences of any other nature. The experiences which are re-creative within the recreation program may be work experiences under other conditions. The individual participating in the experience is the one who distinguishes whether or not the experience is re-creative. If the experience gives the individual a new zest for living, it is re-creative for him.

The space age has opened a new frontier. The picture of yesterday is not the picture of today and the picture of today cannot be the picture of tomorrow. Recreation leaders must indeed take a new look at their discipline, for the picture of recreation is the picture of the future. It is called within the field "recreation" where the potentialities of the individual within new environments will interact to form new ideas. For recreation leaders a most needed competence is the ability to be experimental and creative.

Recreation has a large role in the adult education field. The changing world is opening new possibilities for the adult and he has an eagerness to learn within his particular fields of interest.

The average adult today has time left over from his income-making time in which to participate in re-creative experiences. For such participation he may need space, facilities, equipment, other individuals and instruction. The recreation leaders have new roles in identifying community needs for recreation and in using the combined resources of educational and recreational agencies to meet these needs.

The recreation leader's use of evaluation.   The recreation leader of today and tomorrow must be a creative educator. He must understand the educative process, for the recreation leaders, unhampered by the requirements of traditional education, are able to help the individual grow and develop in his own way in an experience of his own choosing.

Danford [1] in his discussion of the values of recreation states the point of view ". . . that recreation of a superior quality is education of the finest type." He further reports a statement by Jacks[2] that: "The education which is not also recreation is a maimed, incomplete, half-done thing. The recreation which is not also education has no re-creative value."

Competencies in evaluation for the recreation leader include his having a firm understanding of the nature of the individual. He needs to be able to help an individual know where he is in the achievement of his potentialities and help him find the experiences he needs. He should be able to use tools and techniques for finding out about the individual's needs.

The leader in recreation has the same concerns as health education and physical education leaders. He must be able to identify individual goals to provide a worthwhile program, and he needs to be able to assess individual achievement within the experiences provided in order that the individual may know where he is in reaching his goals.

Each teacher or leader in health education, physical education and recreation has his own unique position in each of these fields. The role of the teacher or leader may vary considerably from one situation to another. One person may be assuming responsibilities in all three fields and another may be working as a specialist in only one field. Although purposes and experiences may differ, the primary value, the healthy growth and development of the individual, will remain constant.

In this book tools and techniques for collecting various types of data are described. From these tools the teacher or leader may select those which provide him with the type of evidence he needs in evaluating the achievement of goals.

[1] Howard G. Danford, *Recreation in the American Community* (New York: Harper & Brothers, 1953), p. 118.
[2] Lawrence Pearsall Jacks, *Education Through Recreation* (New York: Harper & Brothers, 1932), p. 2.

Selected References

Health Education

1. Joint Committee on Health Problems in Education of the American Medical Association-National Education Association, *Health Education.* Washington 6, D. C.: National Education Association, 1948.

2. Oberteuffer, Delbert, *School Health Education.* New York: Harper & Brothers, 1949.

Physical Education

3. Cassidy, Rosalind, *Curriculum Development in Physical Education.* New York: Harper & Brothers, 1954.

4. Oberteuffer, Delbert, *Physical Education.* New York: Harper & Brothers, 1956. (Revised Edition.)

Recreation

5. Danford, Howard G., *Recreation in the American Community.* New York: Harper & Brothers, 1953.

2

THE EVALUATION PROCESS

EVALUATION COMPETENCIES

To understand:
1. the meaning of evaluation
2. the foundations for evaluation in health education, physical education and recreation
3. how to evaluate
4. what to evaluate

EXPERIENCES FOR THE STUDENT

1. Study the scientific facts which describe how the individual grows and develops. Make your own deductions from the facts and write value statements with which you agree.
2. Select the values which you will use as the basis for evaluation in health education, physical education and recreation. From these values develop guidelines for the teacher or leader to use in evaluating health education, physical education and recreation.

Evaluation today is perhaps the most important process in the field of education. It is of like importance in the general affairs of mankind, for evaluation is essential to the orderly process of change.

We are living in two worlds. One is described by our understanding of what has been and, one is described by the activity of today and tomorrow. Difficulties arise because decisions made on the basis of the old world are being used in the new world.

For his own good health a person must be able to live within the changes. If he is to do this, he must first be able to identify the values; he must understand *how* and *what* to evaluate in order to determine the course of action which is best under the circumstances. He must understand the meaning of evaluation and be able to apply the process for his own best good and for the good of others.

For the teacher or leader such a responsibility is indeed demanding. He must be able to help others understand how and what to evaluate as a basis for their own actions in addition to identifying and charting his own course of action. He must be competent in the use of the evaluation process if he is to help others achieve their best growth and development.

The Meaning of Evaluation

Value is primary in evaluation. The word, "*e valu* ation" means "*from the value.*" Evaluation is a process of making decisions based on value. The "value" selected for making the "evaluation" describes whether the results will be within the old world, the new world, or a mixture of the two. Values may be used to maintain the *status quo* or may be used to develop creativity and experimentalism. Evaluation may contribute to the development of individual differences or to the regimentation of individuals. The selection of the value is the most responsible task of those participating in the evaluation process.

Because value is primary, the person evaluating must know the value against which he is judging. All measurement tools described in this book, therefore, are shown in relation to value. Responsible evaluation demands this procedure.

Teachers and leaders in health education, physical education and recreation should be competent in constructing instruments relating to the values which are their concerns. They should also be discriminating in the selection of tools developed by others. They should, therefore, understand the meaning of value and its function in the construction and selection of measuring instruments.

The steps of evaluation.   Evaluation is the following process: (*a*) the value or ideal state to be achieved is described relative to the purpose to be accomplished; (*b*) the individual or situation is compared to the ideal state through the use of measuring instruments; (*c*) a conclusion is drawn as to whether the ideal and the real are the same or whether some discrepancy exists.

Measurement and evaluation.   Measurement is the description of existing conditions or *status*. When the existing conditions are compared with the ideal, the results show *evaluation*. If discrepancies exist between the status and the ideal, they describe *need*—goals or problems to be solved.

For example, the basketball coach may want a tall man to play center on the team. Height measures are taken of a number of men. This is *measurement.* A man under six feet in height may be considered to be of little value in this instance, while someone measuring seven feet may be considered to be of great value. This is *evaluation.* If the purpose were to identify a man who could be a jockey at the race track, the man whose measurements were under six feet would be of greater value than the man who measured seven feet in height.

Measurement describes status without placing a value on it. Measurement is essential to evaluation. In evaluation, a purpose is stated, the value is clarified, a measure is taken and results are interpreted in relation to purpose.

Foundations of Evaluation in Health Education, Physical Education and Recreation

In the United States the stated values are those of a democratic philosophy which affirms as primary the worth and dignity of the individual.

Scientific facts which describe how the individual grows and develops include:

1. The individual is born an organic unit who, with the environment, becomes a larger unit (*1, 4, 6, 7, 8, 9, 10, 11, 13, 15*).[1]
2. The individual inherits genes, "maturational determiners," which influence his growth and development from conception to death (*4, 5, 8, 11, 12*).
3. The individual is born with inherited capacities for growth and development which are uniquely his own and which he has a need to realize or actualize (*7, 9, 12, 13*).
4. Each person has a unique pattern of growth (*4, 5, 8, 11*).
5. Individuals follow a general sequence of growth and decline characterized by the species of a culture (*4, 5, 8, 11*).
6. Learning can take place only when maturity allows it (*4, 5, 8, 11*).
7. Nothing springs from the individual alone or from the environment alone, but everything springs from the interaction between the individual and the environment (*12, 13*).
8. Development takes place through both maturation and experience (*4, 5, 8, 11*).

[1] Numbers in parentheses refer to numbered Selected References at the end of each chapter.

9. The individual must have certain materials and conditions to maintain health and to continue to grow and develop (*1, 2, 3, 4, 5, 6, 7, 8, 9, 10, 11, 12, 13, 14, 15*).

Materials and Conditions Necessary
for Healthy Growth and Development (2, 7, 12, 14)

Air
Food
Liquids
Rest, relaxation, sleep
Temperature regulation
Elimination of waste products
Freedom from poisons
Freedom from focal infection
Activity, exploration, manipulation, need to keep going
Perpetuation of the species, procreation
Safety, self preservation, freedom from threat
Taking care of what one is born with
Affection
Belonging and being valued
Success and recognition
Likeness to others and difference from others
Experience and organization of experiences
Orientation to the environment
Completion of incomplete actions
Perceptual clarity
Realization of potentialities

10. Individual growth and development is directed by the interaction of the individual with the environment (*4, 5, 8, 11*).
11. Developmental tasks are goals which arise from the interaction of the individual and his environment. The first developmental task is that of achieving self identity upon which all other developmental tasks rest (*1, 3, 4*).
12. Between the ages of three and five the individual has achieved a beginning self identity, learned through the interaction of the organism and the achievement of the materials and conditions necessary for healthy growth and development (*1, 9*).
13. Having achieved a beginning self identity, the individual makes

selections from his environment which tend to perpetuate his self as he sees it. He continues to grow and develop as the interaction allows (1, 6, 7, 9, 12, 13, 15).

14. The individual who has achieved a healthy self identity is able to achieve new tasks as they arise. Tasks which he may or may not achieve depend upon this initial organization of meaning (1).

Developmental Tasks[2]

Achieving an appropriate dependence-independence pattern
Achieving an appropriate giving-receiving pattern of affection
Relating to changing social groups
Developing a conscience
Learning one's psycho-socio-biological sex role
Accepting and adjusting to a changing body
Managing a changing body and learning new motor patterns
Learning to understand and control the physical world
Developing an appropriate symbol system and conceptual abilities
Relating one's self to the cosmos

15. Each individual has a primary goal, that of enhancing, maintaining, and actualizing the self (1, 6, 7, 15).

16. Individual development is influenced by the aspirations, the picture of what he intends to accomplish in the future (1, 7, 12).

17. Individual motives spring from the need to maintain, enhance and actualize the self (1, 6, 7, 10, 15).

18. The provision of rich experiences within the environment is essential to healthy growth and development and to the achievement of individual potentialities (3, 6, 12, 15).

The individual, therefore, is (a) unique, (b) growing and developing, (c) goal centered and (d) interacting with his environment as a unit.

The goals to be achieved in health education, physical education and recreation are those which contribute to the healthy growth and development of the individual in a democratic society. The values are the philosophical beliefs and the scientific facts about the individual.

[2] Association for Supervision and Curriculum Development, *Fostering Mental Health in Our Schools,* 1950 Yearbook (Washington, D. C.: National Education Association, 1950), pp. 84-87. Quoted by permission.

How to Evaluate

Deductions from the foundations of healthy growth and development provide guidelines for the use of the evaluation process by teachers and leaders in health education, physical education and recreation:

Foundation Facts	*Guidelines for Teacher or Leader*
The worth and dignity of the individual is paramount.	Evaluation should be used to identify individual needs and goals, and these needs and goals should determine experiences.
The individual and the environment are an interacting unit.	Evaluation results should be interpreted from an understanding of the individual in his world—in terms of the total situation in which the evaluation was done.
Each individual is unique.	Evaluation results will show variation from individual to individual. The "value" should be the ideal state for the attainment of individual purposes rather than using one individual as a standard against which to compare another individual.
Each individual has a primary goal of enhancing, maintaining and actualizing the self.	Evaluation should be used to help the individual identify his goals in relation to his aspirations and future desires, rather than to appraise where he is in relation to something he "should have done."
Individual development is influenced by his aspirations.	Evaluation should help the individual see himself as worthy, successful and capable of achieving his potentialities.
The individual tends to perpetuate his "self" as he sees it.	Evaluation results should be interpreted from an understanding of the self identity, recognizing that some

individuals who have not achieved a healthy self identity are even more different from the "normal" than the "normals" are from each other.

Learning takes place only when the individual is ready for it.

Evaluation should be used to identify the individual's readiness.

What to Evaluate

The teacher or leader who is concerned with the healthy growth and development of the individuals with whom he is working will be aware of the need for understanding as much as he can about each individual. The teacher or leader, therefore, must know *who* the individual is, *how* he sees himself and his situation, his goals and his aspirations. He must understand the health status of the individual, his practices and his motives. In addition to this he must have competence in helping individuals identify and clarify their purposes and goals.

The individual and his environment are an interacting unit. The environment may contribute either positively or negatively to the individual's goal achievement. The teacher or leader, therefore, must be competent to evaluate the environments in light of the materials and conditions necessary for the healthy growth and development of the individual. He must have competence in helping individuals assess their areas of need in order that such needs may be met.

Individual goals and experiences for goal fulfillment must be closely related for learning to occur. The teacher or leader, therefore, must be competent in evaluating the specific experiences in his particular field as they relate to individual goal achievement. He must have competence in helping individuals select experiences which will meet their needs and provide solutions to their problems. He must help them understand where they are in goal achievement through particular experiences.

The evaluation competencies needed by the teacher or leader in health education, physical education and recreation, therefore, include: (a) understanding the individual; (b) understanding the environments; and (c) understanding the experiences.

Individual purposes, environments, experiences are interacting and must be examined in such relationship. A teacher or leader in health education, physical education and recreation works with an individual in identifying his goals, selecting experiences best suited for goal achievement in an enviroment conducive to such achievement. It is the purpose of this book to present the evaluation materials in this sequence, retaining the wholeness of the individual in his particular environment.

Selected References

1. Allport, Gordon W., *Becoming*. New Haven: Yale University Press, 1955.

2. Anderson, Harold, (ed.), *Creativity and Its Cultivation*. New York: Harper & Brothers, 1959.

3. Association for Supervision and Curriculum Development, *Fostering Mental Health in Our Schools, 1950 Yearbook*. Washington, D.C.: National Education Association, 1950.

4. Ausubel, David P., *Theory and Problems of Child Development*. New York: Grune and Stratton, 1957.

5. ———, *Theory and Problems of Adolescent Development*. New York: Grune and Stratton, 1954.

6. Combs, Arthur W. and Donald Snygg, *Individual Behavior*, rev. New York: Harper & Brothers, 1959.

7. Goldstein, Kurt, *The Organism*. New York: American Book Company, 1939.

8. Hurlock, Elizabeth B., *Developmental Psychology*. New York: McGraw-Hill Book Company, Inc., 1953.

9. Lewin, Kurt, *A Dynamic Theory of Personality*. New York: McGraw-Hill Book Company, Inc., 1935.

10. Maslow, A. H., *Motivation and Personality*. New York: Harper & Brothers, 1954.

11. Merry, Frieda K. and Ralph V., *The First Two Decades of Life*. New York: Harper and Brothers, 1950.

12. Murphy, Gardner, *Human Potentialities*. New York: Basic Books, Inc., 1957.

13. ———, *Personality*. New York: Harper & Brothers, 1947.

14. Prescott, Daniel A. (Chairman, A Report of the Committee on the Relation of Emotion to the Educative Process), *Emotion and the Educative Process*. Washington, D.C.: American Council on Education, 1938.

15. Snygg, Donald and Arthur W. Combs, *Individual Behavior*. New York: Harper & Brothers, 1949.

PART TWO

Finding out about THE INDIVIDUAL

Competencies Needed by Teachers and Leaders in Health Education, Physical Education and Recreation

1. To understand the assessment of individual status

2. To understand the assessment of individual practices

3. To understand the assessment of individual motives

Objective	Value or Criterion	Measuring Tool
To assess individual status	Healthy growth and development of the whole individual	Medical records Personnel records Autobiography Observation of health status Sociometry Measures of body size and proportions Postural measures Strength measures Endurance measures Relaxation measures Measures of fundamental movement
To assess individual practices	Materials and conditions necessary for healthy growth and development and developmental tasks	Health practice inventory Inventory of inter-personal relations Daily schedule Anecdotal record
To assess individual motives	Motivation theory	Informal conversation Formal interview Unstructured composition Interest inventory Attitude inventory

3

ASSESSMENT OF INDIVIDUAL STATUS

EVALUATION COMPETENCIES

To *understand:*

1. *the types of information available to the teacher from medical records and reports*
2. *the types of information available to the teacher from personnel records*
3. *how to develop and use an autobiography*
4. *how to observe health status*
5. *how to develop and use sociometric instruments*
6. *how to use measures of body size and proportions*
7. *how to appraise postures*
8. *how to measure strength*
9. *how to measure endurance*
10. *how to appraise relaxation*
11. *how to appraise fundamental movement*

EXPERIENCES FOR THE STUDENT

1. *Using the tools described in this chapter, collect data about yourself or another individual. Interpret the data and write a report of individual status.*
2. *Organize into groups. Each group selects one tool for determining status and uses the tool to collect data from the other members, helping them to understand how to develop and administer the tool and interpret the results.*
3. *Invite a resource person, such as a school nurse, doctor, psychiatrist to discuss how to use resource help in interpreting medical and personnel records.*

Since the individual is a whole organism interacting with the environment as a unit, the status of his healthy growth and development is a result of this interaction. The "status" of an individual is described as his state of being or his condition. His status in healthy growth and development is the result of his particular inheritance and the actual materials and conditions necessary for growth and development of which the individual has been able to avail himself.

Assessment of status in this book includes two large areas: (a) appraisal of healthy growth and development accomplished by medical and other student personnel services and (b) appraisal of healthy growth and development undertaken by the teacher or leader in health education, physical education and recreation, including the use of such tools as the autobiography, observation, sociometry, anthropometric measures, strength and endurance measures, relaxation measures and measures of fundamental movement. Health appraisal is considered to be a team approach with each person supplementing the other in a united effort to understand the individual. (6)

The teacher or leader needs to develop particular competencies in understanding and using medical and other student personnel services. These are (a) to understand the type of information available to the teacher from medical records and reports and (b) to understand lines of communication essential in the appraisal of individual status.

Medical Record Information

Medical information may be provided by the school medical personnel or by the individual's personal physician. The Second National Conference on Physicians and Schools[1] recommends that "whenever possible the family physician should conduct the entrance and periodic examinations of school children and perform the diagnostic procedures for those referred for what appear to be specific health problems."

The Joint Committee on Health Problems in Education of the National Education Association and the American Medical Association describes the minimum essentials as including a review of the health history, results of screening tests and an examination of the following conditions and parts of the body:[2]

Nutrition	Muscle tone
Eyes and eyelids	Posture
Ears and eardrums	Bones and joints

[1] American Medical Association, *Second National Conference on Physicians and Schools* (Chicago: Amerian Medical Association, 1949) p. 5.

[2] The Joint Committee on Health Problems in Education of the National Education Association and the American Medical Association, *School Health Services* (Washington 6, D.C.: National Education Association, 1953), p. 42. By permission.

Skin and hair

Heart

Pulse (resting)

Pulse (after exercise)

Lungs

Nervous system

Abdomen

Nose, throat and tonsils

Thyroid gland

Lymph nodes

Teeth and gums

Some students may require a special examination. Athletes, for example, should have special attention. The following is recommended in addition to the usual physical examination given others periodically:

Special attention should be given to the degree of maturation of the child, the heart before and after stressful exercise, the bones and joints with particular reference to their vulnerability in contact sports, the presence of inguinal and umbilical hernias, and if practical, urinalysis and blood pressure determinations. Consideration should be given, also, to a history of rheumatism, heart murmur, pleurisy with effusion, dislocated knee cartilage, and repeated instances of concussion when determining whether or not a youth should participate in athletic activities, particularly in the contact sports.[3]

Recreation leaders, as well as physical education teachers, need to be particularly aware of the results of such an examination since competitive sports are a part of present day recreation. These results provide the information for the criteria for the selection of individuals for participation in the competitive sports program.

The school or family physician keeps a health history on each individual. The health history provided for the school upon the entrance of the child should be complete since it is used as the basis for continuing history reports. An example of a typical health history record follows:

Child's Name_____

Birth Date_____ Sex_____

Father's Name_____ Occupation_____

Mother's Name_____ Occupation_____

Address_____ Phone No._____

Number of Siblings_____ Child's Position_____

Family Physician_____

[3] Joint Committee on Health Problems in Education of the National Education Association and the American Medical Association, *Health Appraisal of School Children, Third Edition* (Washington, D.C.: National Education Association, 1961), p. 39. By permission.

Diseases (please check those contracted by child):

____chickenpox	____measles	____mumps
____diptheria	____smallpox	____asthma
____rheumatic fever	____scarlet fever	____chorea
____whooping cough	____poliomyelitis	____other (list)

Check those diseases against which child has been protected, indicating date of inoculation:

smallpox_____ diptheria_____
poliomyelitis_____ influenza_____
tetanus_____ whooping cough_____
tuberculin test_____ result_____

Check those symptoms frequently displayed by child:

____earache	____gastro-intestinal difficulty
____running ears	____hearing difficulty
____running nose	____visual difficulty
____colds	____sties
____sore throat	____crusted eye-lids
____headache	____toothache
____nail biting	____finger sucking
____temper tantrums	____bed wetting
____speech problem	____Other symptoms (list)

Please list any accidents or operations and indicate date of operation:

_____ date_____
_____ date_____
_____

Comments:

_____
_____
_____

A health history such as this is usually available to the teacher and is very helpful in understanding the child.

Lines of Communication

Lines of communication must be determined in each school or community center so that those working with children, youth or adults have health status information. This information is essential to the clarification of needs and problems of the individual and bears a direct relationship to the individual's selection of experiences. Of particular importance is the report of the health examination from the private physician to the school. Such a report usually includes an explanation of the medical findings which are important to the school and recommendations for the type of program the student may carry, specific restrictions, and special attention he may need.

School health service personnel are usually available for interpreting to teachers and parents through conferences or written reports the results of the health examination. Arrangements should be made in each school for such interpretation.

Teachers and leaders in health education, physical education and recreation should make available to others the information obtained from any assessment of health status for which they are responsible. This material is different in each school depending upon the responsibility taken by medical and other personnel services. All status materials should be filed in the student's cumulative folder. The school doctor will use this information in addition to reports from other teachers and parents in an attempt to understand the individual's health status.

Lines of communication are greatly facilitated if the school or community uses instruction assistants, clerical assistants and general aides to collect and process health data. The teacher then performs only professional duties in utilizing and reporting data on each student.[4]

How to Use Personnel Records

Teachers and leaders should know what kinds of information are available for use from the counseling and guidance services. Tests are available for assessing individual status in conditions such as affection, belonging and being valued, success and recognition, likeness to others and difference from others, orientation to the environment and in such developmental tasks as relate to attaining selfhood. Most of these tests are essentially clinical in nature and require special training to administer and interpret.

The amount and type of data available in a personnel office varies

[4] Trump, J. Lloyd, Director, A Report of the Commission on the Experimental Study of the Utilization of the Staff in the Secondary School, *New Directions to Quality Education* (Washington 6, D.C.: National Association of Secondary School Principals, 1960), pp. 8-12.

markedly from school to school. As with medical records, some of this information is confidential and is not for the use of the teacher.

If a personnel office collects very little information for teacher use, it is most essential that the teacher gather such data as he can.

A survey of four different schools illustrates some types of data which may be available to the teacher in counseling and guidance offices.

The elementary school interviewed had a cumulative record for each child filed in the personnel office. This record included the following information:

1. Physical condition of the child (available from medical records)

2. Adjustment to school (obtained from yearly teacher reports)

3. Information about family, such as siblings, occupation of parents, home conditions (obtained by the teacher in conference with the parents)

4. Information from tests, such as scholastic capacity, mental maturity and achievement in scholastic areas

5. Information about work habits, abilities, interests, emotional control (obtained from observation of the child by the teacher)

No marks were included in this record, but a record of promotions from grade to grade was given. The data collected by the teacher included adjustment to school, information about the family, information from tests and information about work habits, abilities, interests, emotional control. Medical information was collected by the school nurse, using observation techniques and special testing instruments and obtaining other information from the child's personal physician and dentist. There was no medical staff other than the school nurse connected with this school. All personnel records were kept in the office of the principal.

The junior high school interviewed had a special personnel office separate from the office of the principal and staffed by two trained counselors, a man and a woman. The information available in this office included:

1. Cumulative record (obtained from the elementary school attended by the student)

2. Picture of the student

3. Marks received in junior high school

4. Tests of mental maturity and achievement, administered by the classroom teacher and scored and interpreted by the counselors)

5. Autobiography (written in English class)

6. Significant information about growth, adjustment, attitude, attendance (obtained from the classroom teacher)

7. Health card showing results of regular health examinations (administered by the nurse and school physician)

8. Information obtained from student at time of registration in the school
   a. accidents and illnesses
   b. subjects liked best and least
   c. musical accomplishments
   d. participation in programs
   e. jobs held
   f. two best friends
   g. three wishes of what he would like most to have or be

Each student had one interview with a counselor each year, and students with problems were encouraged to request further interviews as needed. Academic advising was done by the counselor in the first interview.

The particular *senior high school* intervewed also had a special personnel office staffed by two counselor-administrators who functioned as the girls' vice principal and boys' vice principal. The duties of these two counselors consisted primarily of program advising each semester and administering disciplinary measures when needed. The data kept in this office included the following:

1. Testing information, including mental maturity, achievement and vocational interest (collected by the homeroom teacher and interpreted by the counselors)

2. Family background, personal goals and interests (obtained in personal interview between student and counselor during program advising)

The information collected from students in this particular high school was used almost exclusively for academic advising.

The university interviewed collected two types of data: (*a*) academic performance data, sent to the student's major department for the use of faculty members who were working with the student; (b) research and counseling data, filed only in the counseling office, confidential in nature and for use by the counselors. These data consisted of the following:

1. Academic performance data
   a. scholastic aptitude test
   b. battery of achievement tests
   c. reading comprehension test
   d. test of critical thinking

2. Research and counseling data
   a. counseling inventory, including personal data about family background, interests, aspirations
   b. personality inventory
   c. personal adjustment inventory
   d. vocational adjustment inventory

Counselors were available to help the faculty members interpret the academic performance data which were sent to them. The research and counseling data were confidential and access to these data was possible only through the written permission of the student.

The materials available to teachers in these four schools consisted chiefly of academic achievement data and scholastic aptitude information. The elementary school and junior high school had information about the family and observations from teachers about the child. The junior high school had additional data which would provide information about the individual's motives and aspirations.

The senior high school, however, had a very meager collection of information for understanding the student. In this particular high school it would be necessary for the teacher to gather additional data to help him understand the student.

The university was the only institution of the four surveyed who collected test data relating to personality adjustment. That the other three did not have these data could be due to lack of a trained staff in the public schools, plus the fact that there are few tests to measure personality or self concepts below the college level.

The relationship between the counseling office and the teaching staff may vary from school to school. The point of view held by some counseling staff members is that the teacher should keep "hands off" everything except purely academic instruction in subject matter areas.

The conviction has been growing in recent years, however, that guidance is the function of all school staff and recreation personnel. Although it is important to have technical staff members who assume responsibility for organizing the guidance program and who collect certain kinds of data, the teacher or leader is in a position to provide constant help and guidance for the individual. The process of teaching implies a guidance approach. The teacher must understand the needs, desires, aspirations of each individual if he is to foster healthy growth and development.

How to Use the Autobiography

The autobiography is a tool which may be used by the teacher or leader to obtain a history of the individual, a picture of his life both past and present. The autobiography may be focused toward any condition in which information is desired. For example:

The Value	*The Information Requested*
Belonging and being valued	1. Experiences which have influenced feelings about himself
	2. Facts about his family life, his feelings about his family
	3. Aspirations and desires he wishes to attain

The physical education teacher may wish to find out about the individual's experiences and feelings concerning movement. An autobiography of movement may contain such information as the following:

The Value	*The Information Requested*
Managing a changing body and learning new motor patterns	1. Activities and movement experiences from earliest recollection to the present
	2. Feeling about gross body movement
	3. Successful experiences in movement
	4. Areas of concern or avoidance in movement experiences

An autobiography of movement written by a student in a college physical education class is presented, with her permission, as an illustration.

MY AUTOBIOGRAPHY OF MOVEMENT

My pre-school movement experiences.   I remember general play with other children, digging, climbing, swinging, and days at the beach. The only specific incident which sticks in my mind occurred one day while I was riding my tricycle by myself on the driveway. Somehow it tipped and the inside of my thigh got caught in the pedal chain. I couldn't get loose and although I yelled and yelled my mother couldn't hear me because she was vacuuming. Finally I jerked loose. Afterwards I wasn't fearful of the tricycle and can't remember any unpleasant aftereffects.

My elementary school movement experiences.   The primary grades are remembered as generally happy ones. I enjoyed group and individual games. But I do remember that I preferred imaginative games, and that in my neighborhood the other children always relied on me to think up new games. However, the intermediate grades were not so happy in relation to movement. At this time several incidents occurred which were pretty painful, and as a result I began to fear group games. I really think the cause of it all was the fact that I was very tall for my age and perhaps because of my rapid growth not very well coordinated. At any rate my skills were practically nonexistent. One day in the sixth grade our physical education supervisor told me in front of the class that I was big enough to hit the ball over the fence. Unfortunately my reputation was well known to the class.

I was afraid to square dance because I was taller than the boys. One day I went to deliver a note to the other sixth grade teacher, and a boy in her class remarked loudly that I was bigger than the teacher. She did nothing to reduce my embarrassment. As a result of this and other similar happenings I came to the conclusion that the less I had to play games, stand up in view of others, run, and even jump rope the less people would notice how tall I was. And so movement practically ceased for me. I couldn't learn to swin because I was afraid to try the strokes in front of other people. The only activity I enjoyed was horseback riding, mainly because I loved the animals. My parents encouraged this, and I developed into a good rider. But I was a mess in all other movement areas. One thing I've never been able to understand is the fact that my best friend from kindergarten to the present time was a natural athlete and is now teaching physical education.

My junior high school movement experiences.   Naturally the experiences I had in the fifth and sixth grades were thoroughly reinforced in junior high. I developed an attitude of not trying as the safest approach. I remember at an eighth grade dance which I had gathered all my courage to attend the boys dared the smallest boy in our class to ask me to dance. I dreaded physical education classes, and when I was forced to play I always tried to avoid getting in a position where I would have to act. I chose right field, because fewer balls came there. I never attempted to make a basket, unless the situation absolutely demanded it.

My high school movement experiences. Everything was the same. My physical education teacher told my mother I would be better off in a home economics class. A couple of things happened that made my attitude a little less fearful about my height and physical activities. My parents enrolled me in a modeling class which emphasized the good points of being tall, and from the exercises in posture and modeling clothes I got over to some degree my self consciousness in front of people. Also I gained a very dear friend in my art teacher. He was the sponsor of a modern dance club, and because of my respect for him, I attended their meetings. But I very seldom participated. If I had such an experience sooner, it would have probably had a great influence on me.

My college movement experiences. I had to fulfill the physical education requirements, but I dreaded doing so. I took courses which didn't involve too much experience. Orientation, fencing, and body mechanics. I didn't do too well in them, but I did enjoy them sometimes. I still dislike group games and even though I have overcome the extreme self-consciousness about my height, sometimes when I am depressed or tired I begin to feel very, very large and ungainly. One thing which has happened is that I have worked as a recreation leader for six summers. I have thoroughly enjoyed playing any and all games with the children. At present I have practically no physical recreation other than walking. I don't swim. My husband tried to teach me tennis, but finally gave up.

A movement autobiography such as this helps the teacher to understand the student's feelings toward movement and the types of experiences he has had. It is usually less threatening for the student to tell what he has done and how he felt at an earlier time than to write his feelings toward a particular activity at the given time.

In this particular situation the teacher and student worked together in identifying specific areas of need which could be met in the class experiences. The university recreational program was also explored as a possible avenue for further experiences in achieving movement goals.

How to Observe Health Status

The appearance and behaviors of the individual will provide information for the teacher or leader in appraising his health status. The results of the medical examination and the health history identify the health problems of the individual. Through health counseling, observation and other techniques for knowing the individual, the teacher may recognize the "normal" health status for that person. When divergencies occur, the teacher will be able to recognize them.

The teacher or leader should set up an immediate plan for getting acquainted with each person. Observation is a tool used for this purpose by all teachers. Too frequently students are appraised on the basis of what a teacher infers from projecting his own feelings into the situation. If a teacher "likes" the student, he tends to see only those things which enhance his picture of what he believes the student really is. If, by chance, he happens to see behavior which does not conform to this picture, he tends to disregard it.

If observation is to be used with any degree of proficiency, it is essential for teachers to learn to observe accurately. They should avoid forming judgments about students and should base conclusions only on concrete evidence. To collect such evidence requires training and practice in observation, accurate recording of observed behavior and ability to analyze and summarize without bias.

The observation should be prepared for ahead of time. The values should be stated, the criteria identified and procedures for observing and recording determined. The observer should watch for significant behavior and record what he sees without interpretation.

In observing the health status of an individual, it is important to recognize the meaning of what *is* a healthy individual. Criteria made up of a long list of health problems are ineffective tools for appraising health status. For example, lists such as these are frequently set up for the teacher to use:

1. Does he have pimples or other blemishes?

2. Do his ears run?

3. Does he have sties?

4. Does he have tics or distracting mannerisms?

5. Does he fall asleep during class?

6. Does he bite his nails?

The teacher should have a picture of what good health means for the individual. Positive health conditions should be used to describe health status, and the teacher should ask, "Does the individual do these things? Does he look like this?"

An illustration of how such a list may be developed follows. One of the conditions for healthy growth and development, "taking care of what one is born with," is used as an example. Some of the factors included in this condition are eyes, ears, nose, teeth and mouth, throat, skin, postures and the like. Criteria are set up to describe the healthy growth and development of "what one is born with."

CHECK LIST FOR OBSERVATION OF HEALTH STATUS

The Values	Criteria Used for Observation of Health	YES	NO
Taking care of what one is born with:			
Eyes	Are his eyes clear and bright?	———	———
	Are lids and lashes clean?	———	———
Ears	Is he usually attentive?	———	———
	Are ears free from discharge?	———	———
Nose	Does he breathe easily through his nose?	———	———
	Is he free from nasal discharge?	———	———
Teeth and mouth	Are lips pink and smooth?	———	———
	Are jaws well-shaped with even bite?	———	———
Throat	Is voice clear and well-modulated?	———	———
	Does he swallow without difficulty?	———	———
Skin	Is his skin smooth and firm?	———	———
	Does his skin glow with good color?	———	———
Postures	Is he erect and confident?	———	———
	Are his movements relaxed?	———	———

Conditions under which observations are made will vary with the situation. Each teacher should find an opportunity to see each student each day. Most elementary school teachers do this easily since they have the children for the entire day. Techniques which have been used by special teachers who work with the student for only a forty-five minute period daily, include:

1. Teacher stands at the door of the classroom and greets each student by name as he enters the room. This gives the teacher an opportunity to look at each student individually; students who appear to be different from usual may be checked more carefully.

2. Teacher talks to students informally while walking out to the playing field and observes them specifically during the activity.

3. Teacher makes an effort to really see each student as he calls roll.

4. Teacher observes students in uncontrolled behavior situations or during informal play or in recreational periods.

Most of these situations are readily available to the health education and physical education teacher, and the recreation leader has numerous opportunities to observe individuals in the recreational programs.

In developing a check list for the observation of health status, the teacher or leader should first select those materials and conditions necessary for healthy growth and development which are related to health status and which are readily observable. He must also select only those conditions that he is competent to appraise, leaving other appraisals to specialists. He must then find out what is meant by good health in these areas and set up criteria against which to check.

The focus of the observation should be on the meaning of health and well-being for the particular individual, rather than on an attempt to check the many thousands of possible divergencies which are so frequently listed as criteria for observation. The important consideration is that the teacher or leader *know* each individual.

Determination of health status, therefore, includes: (*a*) working with the medical personnel to interpret the results of the medical examination and to understand the health condition of each student; (*b*) working with the student through the counseling situation to better understand him and to help him understand his own health status; (*c*) using daily observation to check the health status of each student; and (*d*) referring students with divergencies to medical or specially trained personnel.

How to Use Sociometric Techniques

Sociometric techniques may be used by the teacher or leader to assess individual status in the conditions of affection, belonging and being valued, in likeness to others and in the developmental task of relating to changing social groups. Sociometry is concerned with how the individual relates to others, how he is accepted by others in his particular situation and how he feels about others in his group.

Social distance scales and sociograms are tools for use in studying these social relationships. A very real concern of the teacher or leader is that the students with whom he is working are comfortable and happy in their groups in order that they may work productively on their particular goals. Individuals who are uneasy in their group relationships may find it difficult to realize their potentialities in the particular group structure. Also, a group in which most of the members dislike each other tends to have low morale and consequently low productivity.

Data for the social distance scale and for the sociogram are collected from the group members by having them indicate their feelings about each other.

The social distance scale. To collect data for the social distance scale, each group member is given a check list upon which he indicates his feeling toward every other member of the group. For example:

HOW I FEEL ABOUT OTHERS IN MY GROUP

My Name   John Doe   Grade 7

Place an X in the column which best describes how you feel about each person listed on this page. After your own name, place an X in the column which shows how you feel about yourself.

	Jim A.	John D.	Bob G.	George F.
Would like him for my best friend	___	___	___	___
Would like him for one of my friends	___	___	___	___
He is all right to have around me	___	___	___	___

	Jim A.	John D.	Bob G.	George F.
Don't know him very well	___	___	___	___
Don't like him very much	___	___	___	___
Don't want him around me at all	___	___	___	___

These choices are tabulated and totaled for the group on a master sheet. Numerical values may be assigned to each category for scoring purposes.

		Jim A.	John D.	(Other Students)	(Choices) Totals
+3	Best friend	4	0		18
+2	One of my friends	16	2		190
+1	OK to have around	2	11		156
−1	Don't know him	0	8		68
−2	Don't like him	0	1		72
−3	Don't want him around	0	1		25
Individual Score		46	2		

An interpretation of the data shows that there were 18 "best friend" choices from the people in this particular group. This could mean that 18 different individuals selected someone in the group for a "best friend" or several individuals could have chosen a number of group members for "best friends." An analysis of the individual check sheets gives further information about the choices. There were 190 choices for "one of my friends" and since there were 30 people in the group, some of the individuals chose several group members for "one of my friends."

The totals on the master sheet, therefore, give a picture of group morale. If most of the checks are in the positive columns, the group members appear to like rather than dislike each other. An examination of the data shows 25 "don't want him around me" choices. It is possible that one of the group members is being rejected by many of the other members or one group member may be rejecting 25 members of his group. Again, the indivdual check sheets may be examined to give further information.

For this particular group there is a grand total of 364 positive choices as compared to 165 negative choices which would indicate roughly that the group members feel positive rather than negative toward each other.

The individual scores are obtained by multiplying the number of choices in each category by the category weighting and adding all weighted scores algebraically. For example, the process of computing the score for Jim A. and for John D. is as follows:

<table>
<tr><td>Jim A.</td><td>John D.</td></tr>
<tr><td>$3 \times 4 = 12$</td><td>$3 \times 0 = 0$</td></tr>
<tr><td>$2 \times 16 = 32$</td><td>$2 \times 2 = 4$</td></tr>
<tr><td>$1 \times 2 = 2$</td><td>$1 \times 11 = 11$</td></tr>
<tr><td>$-1 \times 0 = 0$</td><td>$-1 \times 8 = -8$</td></tr>
<tr><td>$-2 \times 0 = 0$</td><td>$-2 \times 1 = -2$</td></tr>
<tr><td>$-3 \times 0 = 0$</td><td>$-3 \times 1 = -3$</td></tr>
<tr><td>46</td><td>2</td></tr>
</table>

An individual's "social distance" in the group may be observed by analyzing the master sheet. For example, Jim A. appears to be quite secure in this particular group. All of the group members have checked him in the positive columns. John D., however, appears to be tolerated by most of the group members with two members showing actual dislike.

An examination of each individual check sheet will give some information on the individual's feelings toward the group and toward himself. If most of the checks are in the negative columns, he is apparently not relating well to these particular group members.

An individual may relate positively to one group and not to another. For example, a student may be forced to work with a group which is much more immature than he is and with whom he has no common interests. The teacher or leader should not arbitrarily assume that such individuals are poorly adjusted. They may be relating very well to other groups of their choice.

The sociogram. The sociogram is a diagram of the social relationships within a group as indicated by individual preferences. Each individual is asked to list his first three choices of group members in order of preference and within a specific situation. For example, each student may be asked to list, in order of choice, the three students he would most prefer to have in his group for physical education class or he may be asked to write the names of the persons with whom he would most like to work in planning a class party or in serving on a committee in health education.

An illustration of a procedure for collecting such information appears on p. 39.

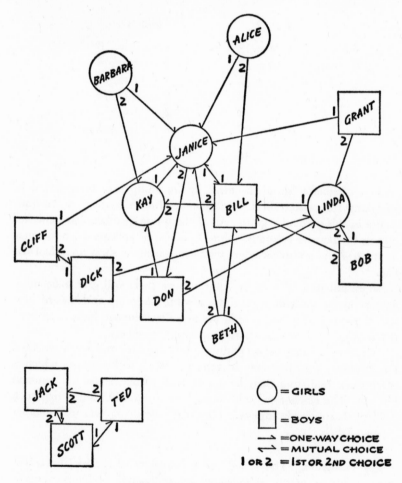

Fig. 3-1. The Sociogram.

Your name_____

We need to set up study committees for our work in nutrition during health education class. It will be more enjoyable for you to work with people whom you like. Write on line 1 the name of the person with whom you would most like to work, on line 2 your second choice, and on line 3 your third choice. In arranging the committees, we shall try to give each person at least one of his three choices.

If there is anyone with whom you would prefer *not* to work, write the name of such a person (or persons) at the bottom of the page.

1._____
2._____
3._____

Prefer not to work with:

_____

_____

A usual procedure in diagramming the choices is to use circles to indicate girls and triangles or squares for boys (*see* Fig. 3-1). If there is a large number of people in the group, building the sociogram may be an unwieldy process. Working with first choices only will simplify the process. After these are diagrammed, the second and third choices may be added to the picture.

It is helpful to place those who are most chosen (the "stars") in the center of the sociogram and the least chosen toward the periphery.

Choices may first be tabulated on a master sheet, such as the following:

		Choices		
Choosers	Alice	Barbara	Bill	(Other Children)
Alice		1	2	
Barbara	1		2	
Bill	2			1

Totals
1st choices
2nd choices

The totals on the master sheet quickly show which people received the most first choices, second choices or rejections, and will facilitate the diagramming procedures.

An analysis of this particular sociogram brought out the following observations:

1. *Are the choices consistent with the expected structure of this age group?*

These were adolescent boys and girls in different stages of development. Group members were developing heterosexual relationships and most of them gave every indication of extreme interest in working them out.

2. *Are there any groups which need to be related to the larger group?*

The group composed of Jack, Scott and Ted was not surprising since these three boys seemed to be maturing more slowly than the other boys in the class and they had different interests. By asking the class to make a third choice, these boys would be forced to choose out of their group and the direction of their choices might give possible clues for helping them relate to the other group members. A third choice would also be helpful in showing the relationship of Janice, Kay and Bill to the other group members. Janice selected outside of the group on her second choice, while Kay and Bill closed the group with their second choices.

3. *Are there any individual members who need help in relating to the group?*

Barbara, Alice, Grant and Beth were not chosen by anyone on either the first or second choices. Again, a third choice might result in someone selecting them and would be helpful in determining how best to relate them to the larger group. Barbara, Alice and Grant have selected Janice as their first choices, and Beth has selected Janice as her second choice. It is possible, therefore, that Janice is the best contact for entry into the group, since her own group position is good. Also, she indicated a willingness to move away from the group by choosing Don as her second choice. Don was unchosen by anyone else.

4. *Do the unchosen individuals have any common factors, such as socio-economic level, religion, race, intelligence, ability, personality traits, participation in extra-curricular activities?*

All of the students in this group were from middle class homes, all were caucasians and of average intelligence. The only observable factor that Barbara, Alice and Beth had in common with each other and different from other girls in the group was level of maturity in social relationships. Barbara and Alice seemed to be more immature than the other girls. Beth was more mature than the other class members and most of her friends were older students in the school. She was frankly bored with her age mates and made no secret of it. Grant's difference was, being a new student in the school, he was in the process of getting acquainted with the other students.

5. *Do the most chosen individuals have any common factors?*

Janice, Kay and Linda were all attractive in appearance and outgoing in personality. Linda differed from the other two in that she was overtly aggressive in her attempts to attract "boy friends." In her first and second choices Linda chose two boys and she was chosen by two boys. A third choice would give insight into Linda's relationships in the group with her own sex mates. Bill was a class leader. Although he was chosen by five girls and by only one boy, observation of his relationships with the boys in the class indicated that he was well-accepted by them.

Janice was the "most chosen" of this group and observation of her role in the class verified this fact. She was an attractive, friendly girl with sensitivity toward others.

In summary, the sociogram gives a picture of the group social structure. Such information helps the teacher or leader select experiences which help individuals develop satisfying peer relationships.

Use of Body Size and Proportions

Early measures of body size were concerned with height and weight in relation to age. Data were gathered on a cross section of children and youth and mean height and weight measures were computed for different age groups. These were reported in age-height-weight tables.

Although these tables were based upon averages, they were used as standards against which an individual was measured, with no consideration given to type of body structure, muscle tissue and fat development.

Recognition of individual differences in body proportions resulted in the development of anthropometric measures to identify body types. Such measures include width of chest, shoulder and hip; breadth of knee; and girth of upper and lower arm, wrist, thigh, calf and ankle. Development of fat on the abdomen and at the waist is also used to determine body type.

An example of the use of body structure to determine nutritional status is the Pryor Width-Weight Tables (18) which uses the thoracic and bi-iliac diameters, age and height to determine normal weight for the individual. One of the more recent examples of the use of body types is Sheldon's somatotyping procedure, resulting in three major body types: (a) ectomorph, or linear body type; (b) mesomorph, or heavy, athletic type; and (c) endomorph, or lateral body type (21).

There is controversy in respect to the value of anthropometric measures. Some writers state that it is erroneous to assume that individual growth status can be evaluated by age-height-weight averages alone, since each individual has a unique structure and a unique growth pattern. Other writers on growth and development say that it is possible to estimate with considerable accuracy the developmental level of an individual at a particular chronological age since growth patterns of normal children tend to follow similar lines. The term, "growth," refers to increase in body size, and "development" refers to maturation.

A major criticism of the use of anthropometric measures, or age-height-weight tables, is based upon the concept that individual growth changes are more significant when analyzed in respect to the individual pattern than are comparisons with a group norm. The reliability of anthropometric measures is also open to question. This relates to the precision of the measuring instrument and to the skill of the person doing the measuring. For example, trochanteric hip width is taken from the subcutaneous prominence of the trochanter. Most directions for use of the caliper in taking this measure state that it should be brought into "easy contact" with the trochanter without application of pressure. In some persons the trochanter may be difficult to find. The interpretation of "easy contact" may also make considerable difference in the resulting measure. One researcher used the caliper to measure a post three times in succession and obtained three different measurements.

In an effort to use the individual growth pattern as an estimate of nutritional status, Wetzel (23, 24) constructed a chart for analysis of individual growth curves. By using age, height and weight data one can record individual growth and analyze it according to the body type or "channel." If the individual continues to progress within his own channel, it is assumed that his health picture is good. If he moves from his own channel of growth to another channel, a medical diagnosis is made to determine the cause.

A similar chart has been developed by a Joint Committee on Health Problems in Education of the National Education Association and the American Medical Association. This chart has height-age channels and weight-age channels. If an individual's height falls in a different channel from his weight or if he does not progress steadily within his particular height and weight channels, medical diagnosis is made to determine the reasons for the discrepancies. (*See* Figs. 3-2 and 3-3.)

The ideal body proportions have long been a matter of interest and of controversy. The criteria vary from culture to culture and from decade to decade within the same culture. Within the last fifty years in the United States the "ideal" proportions for the female figure have varied considerably with each era having its stereotype as personified by a particular famous "beauty" of the times. The ideal male figure has remained more stable, but extremes of over-developed musculature particularly in the chest, shoulders and arms have occurred from time to time.

Much of the study of body proportions has been from the standpoint of beauty, artistic or otherwise, rather than from considerations of body symmetry, growth and nutrition.

Ideal proportions for an individual may well be assessed according to the following criteria:

1. Is the body esthetically pleasing to the individual himself?

2. Is the body symmetrical?

3. Are the muscles firm without undue fat deposits or "over-development" which hinder movability?

Two essential measures for determining growth and nutritional status are height and weight, with weight change being one of the best single indicators of nutritional status. Procedures for obtaining accurate height and weight measures are described.

How to measure height. Body length is usually determined by measuring the height of the individual in a standing position. When using beam scales to determine height, the following procedures are used:

1. Directions to person being measured:
Remove shoes
Stand on scales, back to standard
Place feet together, toes pointed forward
Stand erect, chin in horizontal position

2. Directions to person obtaining measurement:
Raise measuring rod above the subject's head

PHYSICAL GROWTH RECORD FOR BOYS

Prepared by the Joint Committee on Health Problems in Education of the NEA and AMA, using data prepared by Howard V. Meredith, State University of Iowa. Additional copies may be secured through the order department of the American Medical Association, 535 N. Dearborn St., Chicago 10, Illinois, or of the National Education Association, 1201 Sixteenth St., N. W., Washington, D. C.

PURPOSE OF RECORD: To supply interesting and helpful information regarding the growth

of _____   _____
        (school boy's name)   (date of birth)

HOW CHILDREN SHOULD BE MEASURED:

Directions for determining weight. If available, use beam-type, platform scales. At the beginning of each examination period check the scales and, in the event they are out of balance, adjust them. Have the boy remove shoes, and coat or sweater. Request the subject to stand in the center of the platform of the scales. Determine weight to the nearest one-half pound.

Directions for measuring height. Use a measure fixed in the upright position, and a wooden headpiece having two faces at right angles. The measure may be a yardstick or an accurate measuring tape fastened either on a special board or (if there is no projecting wainscoting) directly on a smooth wall. While it is possible to use a cigar or chalk box as a headpiece, it is recommended that one be made of more satisfactory design.* Measure height with shoes removed. Have the boy stand with heels, lower back, shoulders and rear of head in contact with the wall or board; heels nearly together but not touching each other; arms hanging at the sides in a natural manner and the head facing straight forward. When the subject is in position, place one face of the headpiece against the board or wall and bring the other face down, keeping it horizontal, until it makes firm contact with the top of his head. See that the heels are kept in contact with the floor and the trunk is maintained in "non-slumped" contact with the measure. Take two separate height measurements on each boy. Record height to the nearest one-fourth inch.

HOW TO USE THE RECORD:

Registering height and weight status. Example: Assume this is the record of Don Jones. Don weighs 43 pounds, is 44 inches in height, and has just had his 5th birthday.

Height

a) On page 2 find age 5 along the *top* of the chart.
b) Locate 44 *inches* along the *upper* left-hand margin.
c) Plot a point *under* the 5 and opposite 44.
d) Just *above* this dot on the HEIGHT graph write "44.0."

Weight

a) On page 2 find age 5 along the *bottom* of the chart.
b) Locate 43 *pounds* along the *lower* left-hand margin.
c) Plot a point *above* the 5 and opposite the 43.
d) Just *below* this dot on the WEIGHT graph write "43.0."

_____

* Specifications may be secured from the Bureau of Health Education of the American Medical Association.

Reproduced by permission of the Joint Committee on Health Problems in Education of the National Education Association and the American Medical Association.

Fig. 3-2.

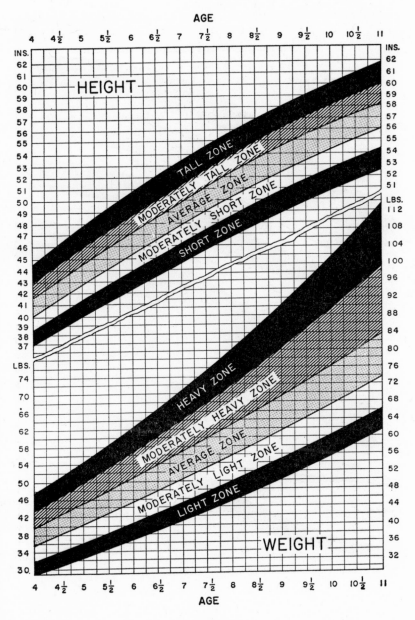

Fig. 3-2 (cont.).

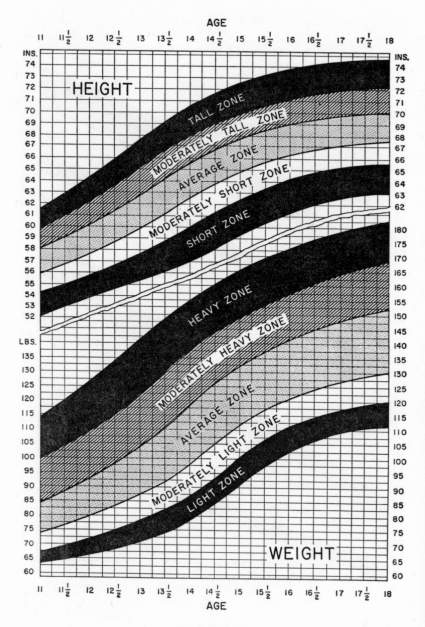

Fig. 3-2 (cont.).

Registering height and weight progress. **Example:** Assume Don is now six months older—at age 5¼ years his weight was 44½ pounds, now at 5½ years he weighs 46 pounds and has a height of 45¼ inches. Further, assume that points representing Don's height at 5½ and his weight at 5¼ and 5½ have been plotted at the appropriate places on page 2. Having records at more than one age, it is now possible to draw curves of progress. Don's progress over the age period 5 to 5½ years may be shown by drawing lines connecting (a) the two points on the height graph and (b) the three points on the weight graph.

HOW TO INTERPRET THE RECORD:*

Interpreting status. 1. The measurement figures written above or below each plotted point provide a ready description of each boy's actual height and weight at all of the ages measurements have been taken.

2. The zones in which a boy's height and weight points for a given age are located indicate his standing, in relation to other boys of the same age. The sample values given at 5 years show Don to fall in the "average zone" for both height and weight.

3. Whenever a boy's height and weight points do not fall in like zones (e. g., tall and heavy, short and light), the dissimilarity may indicate stockiness or slenderness of build and/or it may furnish an important lead regarding state of health. To illustrate, suppose at the time of first measurement, the height point of (Pat Thomas) is found to lie in the "average zone" and his weight point in the "light zone." Pat should be referred to a physician for examination. It may be he is a healthy child of slender build. On the other hand, he may have some infection, need an improved diet, or require changes in his daily living habits.

Interpreting progress. 1. The difference between a boy's heights (or weights) at two different ages shows the amount of change that has taken place during the interval. For example, Don Jones, between 5 and 5½ years of age gained 1¼ inches in height and 3 pounds in weight.

2. The relation of a boy's height or weight curve to the curves on page 2 gives some idea as to whether or not he is growing satisfactorily. To explain: Individual curves for height should run about parallel with the height lines on the chart. For this reason, if (Jim Smith's) curve falls along the middle of the "moderately short zone" over the age period 5 to 8 years and then tends sharply toward the "short zone" (due to a gain between 8 and 8½ of only ¼ to ½ inch), his growth after age 8 obviously warrants medical investigation. Although semi-annual weight growth is often less regular than height growth, an individual weight curve which shows a downward dip (loss of weight) or remains level (failure to gain) is sufficient reason for referring the boy to a physician.

3. The alignment of an older boy's height and weight curves with the zone paths on page 3 show satisfactory growth if one allows for the individual differences in the time at which the adolescent "growthspurt" may occur. That is, interpretations over the age period 11 to 18 years (page 3) are no different from those for the period 4 to 11 (page 2) except that attention must be given to variations in the age at which the adolescent "spurt" may take place. Assume Ted, Bill, and Dick are alike in both height and weight at each age from 4 to 11 years—Ted may begin more rapid height and weight growth before 13, Bill around 14, and Dick not until 15. It follows that as long as Bill and Dick are continuing steady growth at their childhood rates, this growth should not be judged "unsatisfactory."

* *A complete description of the charts is given in "A Physical Growth Record for Use in Elementary and High Schools" reprinted from the American Journal of Public Health, 1949, 39, 878-885.*

372dgh60e25

Fig. 3-2 (concluded).

PHYSICAL GROWTH RECORD FOR GIRLS

Prepared by the Joint Committee on Health Problems in Education of the NEA and AMA, using data prepared by Howard V. Meredith, State University of Iowa. Additional copies may be secured through the order department of the American Medical Association, 535 N. Dearborn St., Chicago 10, Illinois, or of the National Education Association, 1201 Sixteenth St., N. W., Washington, D. C.

PURPOSE OF RECORD: To supply interesting and helpful information regarding the growth

of _____   _____
          (school girl's name)   (date of birth)

HOW CHILDREN SHOULD BE MEASURED:

Directions for determining weight. If available, use beam-type, platform scales. At the beginning of each examination period check the scales and, in the event they are out of balance, adjust them. Have the subject remove shoes, and sweater or jacket. Request her to stand in the center of the platform of the scales. Determine weight to the nearest one-half pound.

Directions for measuring height. Use a measure fixed in the upright position, and a wooden headpiece having two faces at right angles. The measure may be a yardstick or an accurate measuring tape fastened either on a special board or (if there is no projecting wainscoting), directly on a smooth wall. While it is possible to use a cigar or chalk box as a headpiece, it is recommended that one be made of more satisfactory design.* Measure height with shoes removed. Have the girl stand with heels, lower back, shoulders and rear of head in contact with the wall or board; heels nearly together but not touching each other; arms hanging at the sides in a natural manner and the head facing straight forward. When she is in position, place one face of the headpiece against the board or wall and bring the other face down, keeping it horizontal, until it makes firm contact with the top of her head. See that the heels are kept in contact with the floor, that the trunk is maintained in "non-slumped" contact with the measure, and that no obstruction (e. g., comb, clasp, ribbon, or braid) prevents contact with the head. Take two separate height measurements on each girl. Record height to the nearest one-fourth inch.

HOW TO USE THE RECORD:

Registering height and weight status. Example: Assume this is the record of Dora Jenks. Dora weighs 42 pounds, is 43 inches in height, and has just had her 5th birthday.

Height

a) On page 2 find age 5 along the *top* of the chart.
b) Locate 43 *inches* along the *upper* left-hand margin.
c) Plot a point *under* the 5 and opposite 43.
d) Just *above* this dot on the HEIGHT graph write "43.0."

Weight

a) On page 2 find age 5 along the *bottom* of the chart.
b) Locate 42 *pounds* along the *lower* left-hand margin.
c) Plot a point *above* the 5 and opposite the 42.
d) Just *below* this dot on the WEIGHT graph write "42.0."

_____
* Specifications may be secured from the Bureau of Health Education of the American Medical Association.

Reproduced by permission of the Joint Committee on Health Problems in Education of the National Education Association and the American Medical Association.

Fig. 3-3.

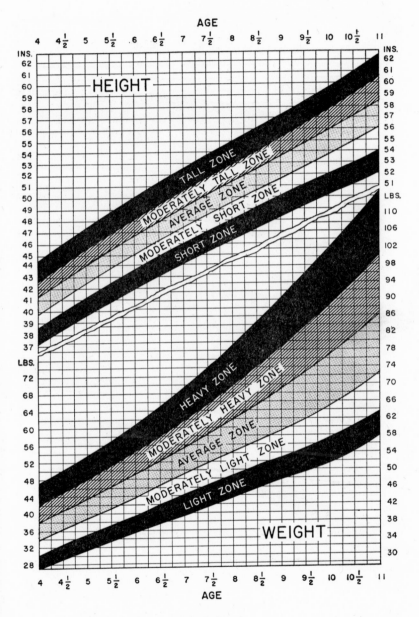

Fig. 3-3 (cont.).

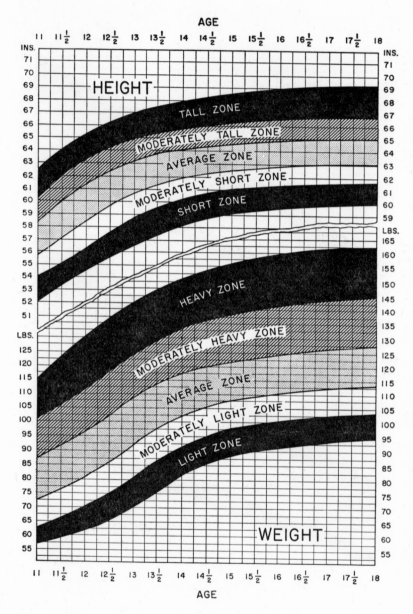

Fig. 3-3 (cont.).

Registering height and weight progress. Example: Assume Dora is now six months older—at age 5¼ years her weight was 43½ pounds; now at 5½ years she weighs 45 pounds and has a height of 44¼ inches. Further, assume that points representing Dora's height at 5½ and her weights at 5¼ and 5½ have been plotted at the appropriate places on page 2. Having records at more than one age, it is now possible to draw curves of progress. Dora's progress over the age period 5 to 5½ years may be shown by drawing lines connecting (a) the two points on the height graph and (b) the three points on the weight graph.

HOW TO INTERPRET THE RECORD:*

Interpreting status. 1. The measurement figures written above or below each plotted point provide a ready description of each girl's actual height and weight at all of the ages measurements have been taken.

2. The zones in which a girl's height and weight points for a given age are located indicate her standing, in relation to other girls of the same age. The sample values given at 5 years show Dora to fall in the "average zone" for both height and weight.

3. Whenever a girl's height and weight points do not fall in like zones (e. g., tall and heavy, short and light), the dissimilarity may indicate stockiness or slenderness of build and/or it may furnish an important lead regarding state of health. To illustrate, suppose at the time of first measurement the height point of (Mary White) is found to lie in the "average zone" and her weight point in the "light zone." Mary should be referred to a physician for examination. It may be she is a healthy child of slender build. On the other hand, she may have some infection, need an improved diet, or require changes in her daily living habits.

Interpreting progress. 1. The difference between a girl's heights (or weights) at two different ages shows the amount of change that has taken place during the interval. For example, Dora Jenks between 5 and 5½ years of age gained 1¼ inches in height and 3 pounds in weight.

2. During the period from age 4 years to age 9 years, information on satisfactoriness of growth is given in the relation of a girl's height and weight curve to the curves on page 2. To explain: Up to age 9, individual curves for height should run about parallel with the height lines on the chart. For this reason, if (Jane Sneed's) curve falls along the middle of the "moderately short zone" over the age period 4 to 7 years and then tends sharply toward the "short zone" (due to a gain between 7 and 7½ of only ¼ to ½ inch), her growth after age 7 obviously warrants medical investigation. Although semi-annual weight growth is often less regular than height growth, an individual weight curve which shows a downward dip (loss of weight) or remains level (failure to gain) is sufficient reason for referring the girl to a physician.

3. Beyond age 9 years, the alignment of a girl's height and weight curve with the zone paths on pages 2 and 3 shows satisfactory growth providing one allows for the known individual differences in the time at which the adolescent "growth-spurt" may occur. That is, interpretations after age 9 are no different from those for the years 4 to 9 except that attention must be given to variations in the age at which the adolescent "spurt" may take place. Assume Nancy, Jill, and Ruth are alike in both height and weight at each age from 4 years to 9 years—Nancy may begin her more rapid growth in height and weight before 11, Jill around 12, and Ruth not until 13. It follows that as long as Jill and Ruth are continuing steady growth at their childhood rates, this growth should not be judged "unsatisfactory."

* *A complete description of the charts is given in "A Physical Growth Record for Use in Elementary and High Schools" reprinted from the American Journal of Public Health, 1949, 39, 878-885.*

Fig. 3-3 (concluded).

Lower cross bar, passing through the hair, to just clear the crown of the head

Read and record the height to the nearest one-eighth inch on the vertical scale on the height rod

When using a wall measure to determine height, proceed as follows:

1. Directions to person being measured:

   Remove shoes

   Stand with back to the wall with heels, buttocks, shoulders and head touching the wall

   Stand erect with chin in horizontal position

2. Directions to person obtaining measurement:

   Mark the wall or attach a yardstick to the wall. Recheck the measuring instrument after it has been placed on the wall. Use a wall that does not have a baseboard or other abutments.

   Use a square which can be placed against the wall and through the hair to just clear the crown of the head.

   Read and record the height to the nearest one-eighth inch.

How to measure weight. Weight varies from day to day and from time to time throughout the day. To achieve greater accuracy it is important to: (a) weigh at regular intervals; (b) weigh at approximately the same time of day with reference to meals and evacuation; (c) weigh with the same amount of clothing on at each time of weighing (accuracy is greater if the subject is disrobed); and (d) use the beam type of scales when possible rather than the spring scales.

1. Directions to person being weighed:

   Remove all clothing if possible. If clothing is kept on, be sure to remove shoes and any heavy sweaters and empty the pockets. Be sure the clothing is the same for each weighing.

   Stand on scales facing scale marker

2. Directions to person obtaining measurement:

   Be sure scales are properly balanced before weighing

   Have subject remove shoes and any other heavy clothing (it is preferable if he is weighed disrobed)

   Move balance bar until scales balance and record to nearest one-half pound

To summarize, limiting or contributing factors to the achievement of individual purposes or aspirations include body size and proportions.

The obese child may have difficulty in establishing satisfying social relationships, partially because of his appearance and also because of his inability to participate in status activities such as games and motor skill areas. The underweight or poorly muscled child may have similar problems.

Each individual should be aware of his own unique structure and his particular growth pattern, of his limitations and his strengths. He needs to understand what he is by nature, what heredity has given him. By understanding his own structure he may better achieve his aspirations, and he may better use that with which he was born.

How to Appraise Postures

Acquiring and maintaining effective use of the body is closely related to the individual's postures. The child is repeatedly admonished by adults to "stand up straight," "stop slumping in your chair." Although many parents and teachers have an uneasy feeling that posture has something to do with health, present and future, their understandings are vague in this area and their "nagging" is usually mostly concerned with appearance. In our culture beauty and charm are associated with the erect posture, head held high. It is with this thought that the command, "stand up straight" is given.

Posture is an area in which everyone believes that something should be done but few are competent to do it. At one time, posture pictures and other posture analyses were in vogue, resulting in stacks of data collected to gather dust in many high school and university physical education and medical files. Most of these materials assessed only standing posture with no analysis of dynamic postures. Many times postural evaluations have been made but because of lack of information and time nothing has been done to correct the divergencies.

Most teachers and leaders in health education, physical education and recreation have had at least a minimal training in gross screening of postures. The items usually included in a gross screening of static posture are alignment of the body, head and neck, comparative height of the shoulders, spinal deviations, pelvic tilt, knees, ankles, legs, arches and feet (11, 16). An example of such a postural examination record is shown in Figure 3-4.

Useful instruments for judging alignment which are readily accessible and inexpensive are the plumb line and the architect's adjustible curve ruler.

The plumb line may be quickly constructed by tying a piece of metal to a string. When this is held vertically, body tilts and torsions may be observed. For good alignment, as seen from the side view of the individual, the line should extend from the lobe of the ear through the point of the shoulder, the hip joint, the rear of the patella, slightly in front of the ankle and halfway between the heel and ball of the foot.

The Davenport adjustable curve ruler (No. 2, 30″) may be obtained

UNIVERSITY OF CALIFORNIA, LOS ANGELES
Department of Physical Education • Developmental Division
CASE ANALYSIS

Disability_____

Physician's Recommendations_____

_____ Code Classification 1 2 3 4 5 6 7 8 9 0
(Health Service)
Other conditions_____

_____ Duplicate conditions: 1 2 3 4

RESULTS AND DISPOSITION

Date entered Developmental_____ Date discharged_____

Results by semesters:	1	2	3	4	Other
Disability corrected					
Disability Improved					
Preventive program					
To Reg. Phys. Educ.					
Temporary assignment					
Left school					
Remarks					

NUTRITIONAL STATUS	Freshman		Sophomore		Junior		Senior		Other
Semester	1	2	1	2	1	2	1	2	
Age (Yrs.–Mos.)									
Height (Inches)									
Pelvic (Width cm.)									
Chest (Width cm.)									
Weight (Normal)									
Weight (Actual)									
Weight (Variation)±									

FOLLOW UP EXAMS	DATES CHECKED	*RESULTS	EXAMINATION	DATES CHECKED	*RESULTS
Blood Pressure			Spine		
Heart			Tracings		
Cardiogram			Flexible Rule		
Others			Anthropometric (Specify)		
X-ray			1.		
Photography			2.		
Posture			3.		
Special			4.		
Foot			Nutritional		
Tracings			Diet Analysis		
Pedograph			Basal Metab.		
Others			Others		
Joint Measurements					
Calipers					
Goniometer					
Tracings					

CODE USED ON CARD
1° = Noticeable–Slight—(Brown tab)   1st Exam = Black
2° = Moderate—(Blue tab)   2nd Exam = Orange
3° = Severe—(Red tab)   3rd Exam = Green
* Results of Follow-up examinations.   4th Exam = Purple

Courtesy of Carl Haven Young.

Fig. 3-4.

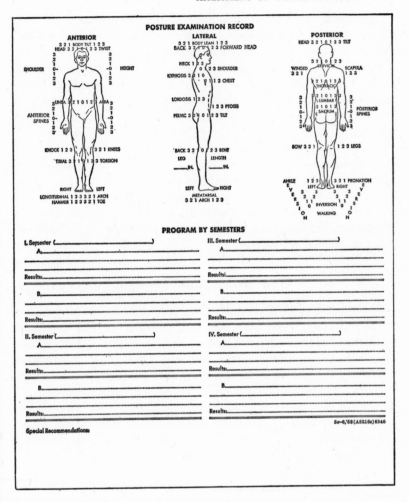

Fig. 3-4 (concluded).

from shops carrying architect's supplies. This rule will show a picture of the anterior-posterior alignment of the neck and back by pressing it firmly against the back, starting at the head and moving downward. The obtained outline may be traced on a piece of paper and the student may see a picture of his back curves. This may be a permanent record against which to compare later tracings.[5]

[5] Charles L. Lowman and Carl Haven Young, *Postural Fitness* (Philadelphia: Lea & Febiger, 1960), pp. 145, 146.

The teacher or leader should refer to medical personnel any cases which appear to be problems, recognizing that it is the function of the medical personnel to diagnose and treat such disorders.

Procedures for assessing dynamic postures employ the use of rating scales. The individual is rated as he walks, sits, picks up objects, climbs stairs. Such rating scales or check lists may be readily constructed by the teacher or leader who has an understanding of the principles of posture and body mechanics. The criteria must first be determined for the "ideal" posture and body mechanics under these various conditions and for the particular age level being rated. A check list or rating scale may then be constructed for individual ratings.

Wells[6] formulates some postural principles which may be useful to the teacher or leader who is constructing such a check list. She concludes that individual differences in structure negate any "single detailed description of good posture."

How to Measure Strength

Muscular strength is needed by the individual for the performance of his daily tasks. If he has a reserve of muscular strength in addition to that needed for his normal requirements, he is able to perform these tasks with greater efficiency and ease. He is also better able to move effectively for prolonged periods in case of emergency.

Such a reserve makes it possible for the individual to broaden his movement experiences since he has the strength necessary for the successful performance of new tasks. Without this reserve he may be unable to participate in many worthwhile experiences because of strength limitations.

Muscular strength is developed by exercising the muscle against increasing resistance. This resistance may be provided by using weights, springs or the weight of the body itself. When muscles are used against increasing resistance, they increase in size. Differences in individuals will cause differences in muscular development, both in degree of development and rapidity of development.

Individual goals include being able to manage one's body with ease and efficiency in the performance of daily tasks and the ability to meet survival demands which may be of a strenuous nature. Strength tests may be used to provide experiences in which the individual studies his

[6] Katharine F. Wells, *Kinesiology*, *2nd Ed.* (Philadelphia: W. B. Saunders Company, 1955), pp. 360-374.

own strength problems and needs. He makes a plan for developing a strength reserve, for developing the strength needed to participate in new movement areas or to develop necessary strength to withstand fatigue in the performance of daily tasks. When he has developed his strength reserve, he may re-test from time to time to determine if he is maintaining this reserve.

When a student is unsuccessful in the performance of a particular movement pattern or when fatigue problems are apparent, strength tests may help to identify the problem. For example, a student may be unable to successfully perform a free throw in basketball. Use of a test of shoulder girdle strength may reveal a weakness in this muscle group. By strengthening these muscles, the student may find that he has improved his ability to perform this skill. If the strength test reveals, however, that the student has adequate strength in these muscles, further diagnosis is needed to determine the problem which may be related to poor mechanics or lack of interest.

Selection of strength tests presents certain problems to the teacher or leader. Instruments for testing strength can be expensive and many schools do not provide them. When instruments and special equipment are used, only one student may be tested at a time, which is not practical in many teaching situations.

Another problem deals with the selection of strength standards. How strong should a person be? Standards for total strength and for strength of specific muscle groups are based on test scores with consideration usually given to the age, height and weight of the subjects.

There is need for research of a basic nature to provide better information relating to strength needs of individuals and for applied research in the area of test construction, with emphasis on the development of tests to be used in teaching-learning situations rather than as research tools.

For the purpose of this book, strength tests have been selected on the basis of the following criteria:

1. Uses no equipment or only equipment which is readily available in most schools

2. Tests large groups at one time rather than one person at a time

3. Is easily scored

4. Is of a level of difficulty which makes it possible for most individuals to obtain a score better than zero

5. Is self-testing in nature and may be used by the person as a practice device

6. Is not hazardous to the performer under normal conditions

7. Has educational value in helping individuals recognize needs and evaluate improvement

Arm and shoulder strength tests.   Arm and shoulder strength may be measured by the push-up and by the pull-up. The three most common ways of performing the push-up in order of difficulty, beginning with the easiest, are (*a*) push-up from the knees, (*b*) push-up from the toes and (*c*) dipping on the parallel bars. The teacher or leader should help the individual select the form of push-up that is within his ability to perform, and as the individual is able to master one form, he may then progress to a more difficult form.

Descriptions of the push-up may be found in much of the testing information. Push-ups from the knees are usually recommended for women and dipping is recommended for men. It is certainly possible, however, that some boys and men may need to start with the easier forms of push-up before progressing to dipping and that some girls and women might well be able to perform dipping with ease. It is important for the individual to select a form in which he can make better than a zero score, moving to more challenging forms as he attains competence.

1. *Push-up from the knees:*

Lie on mat, face down, with hands under shoulders and knees bent. If a mat is not used, protect the knees by placing a cushion such as a folded towel or sweat shirt under them.

On starting signal, extend arms until straight, keeping body in a straight line from head to knees (abdomen should not sag). Weight is supported on hands and knees.

Bend arms and touch chest to floor.

Continue raising and lowering body for as long as possible without stopping.

Score is the total number of completed push-ups (up and down counts as one push-up) which are done *correctly* before stopping.

2. *Push-up from the toes:*

Squat; place hands on floor directly under shoulders with arms straight.

On starting signal, move feet backward, legs straight, supporting body weight on hands and toes. Keep body straight from head to feet throughout entire performance.

Bend arms and touch chest to the floor; then straighten arms, keeping body straight. Continue raising and lowering body for as long as possible.

Score is the total number of completed push-ups (up and down counts as one push-up) which are done *correctly* before stopping.

3. *Dipping on parallel bars:*

Parallel bars are adjusted to shoulder height. Face bars, placing hands at ends of bars. On starting signal, jump to front support position with arms fully extended.

Lower body until arms are bent at a right angle; then push back to original front support position, arms fully extended. Continue dipping as long as possible.

Score is the total number of completed dips (up and down counts as one dip) which are done *correctly* before stopping.

Arm and shoulder strength may also be measured by the pull-up. Use of the horizontal bar for chinning is the most familiar form of the pull-up. This is done by hanging from the horizontal bar at a height which does not allow the feet to touch the floor. This may be made less difficult by using a position which allows part of the weight to be supported by the feet. The test information describes two ways in which this is commonly done, one in which the feet are flat on the floor with the knees bent, hands gripping the bar with the arms straight and the weight supported by the feet and hands. Another form of this test had the hands grasping the bar with arms straight and weight resting on the heels, with the body in a straight line. Both of these forms are combined in the description given here, and the individual may select the form that is most comfortable for him.

As in the push-up, the testing information usually separates these tests by recommending chins for men and pull-ups with support for women. Each person should select the test which will help him evaluate his own competency, and it may be essential for many individuals to use the easier form first.

1. *Pull-up with support:*

Adjust the bar to the height of the sternum apex (breastbone) when the person is standing erect.

Grasp the bar, palms upward. Move feet under bar until weight rests on feet with knees bent (or on heels with knees straight if preferred.) Back should be straight and body and arms should form a right angle.

Pull up to bar until chest touches bar; then extend arms to original position. Continue for as long as possible. With the bent-knee position, the movement is from the knees, and with the weight on the heels with knees straight the movement is from the ankles. Back is straight in either position.

Score is the total number of pull-ups (up and down counts as one pull-up) which are done *correctly* before stopping.

2. *Chinning without support:*

Hang from the horizontal bar, using either forward or reverse grip and at height which does not allow feet to touch floor.

Pull up until chin is over bar; then lower body to hanging position. Continue for as long as possible. Pull should be straight up and down without kipping, kicking or swinging the body.

Score is number of full chins (up and down counts as one chin) completed before stopping.

The grip strength test. The grip strength test violates two of the criteria set up for selection of tests in that it uses special equipment and only one person may be tested at one time. The inclusion of this test is important, however, since grip strength is a good, single measure of total body strength,[7] the test may be administered very rapidly to individual subjects, and the equipment is not so expensive as to be prohibitive for most schools to acquire.

Grip strength is measured by an instrument called a hand dynamometer (or manuometer) which consists of springs mounted between steel bars curved to fit in the hand. The scale is from 0 to 200 pounds.

The dynamometer is held in the hand with the dial toward the palm and the dial hand set at 0. Any movement may be used while squeezing the dynamometer provided the hand or arm does not touch any object, including the body. A movement which is frequently used is the "uppercut." The score is the number of pounds recorded on the scale.

The abdominal strength test. The most common test of abdominal strength which may be done without special equipment is the sit-up. In this test, the person moves from a back-lying position to a sitting position. There are numerous variations of the test.

It is generally accepted that when the legs are in a straight position the test is measuring the abdominal and psoas muscles. When the knees

[7] Wayne Van Huss and others, *Physical Activity in Modern Living* (Englewood Cliffs, N. J.: Prentice-Hall, Inc., 1960) p. 16.

are bent, the abdominals are being measured. Another variation is to raise the legs rather than the torso, which tests the strength of the psoas and lower abdominals.

The form described here appears to be one of the more acceptable forms for measuring isotonic contraction of the abdominal muscles.

1. Sit on the floor with knees bent. Partner holds feet in position on the floor. Hands on shoulders with elbows touching knees.

2. Lie on back, keeping hands on shoulders. Curl trunk forward and sit up, touching elbows to knees. Continue moving from back-lying to sitting position for as long as possible.

3. Score is total number of completed sit-ups (up and down counts as one sit-up) which are done correctly before stopping.

In summary, muscular strength is developed by exercising the muscle against increasing resistance. The individual will develop the muscular strength necessary for performance of his daily tasks since the process of carrying on his work will cause this development. If he is to obtain and maintain reserve strength, he must work his muscles regularly against increased resistance above and beyond that necessary for carrying on his daily tasks. Strength tests help him evaluate his strength achievement for purposes of identifying his strength needs and appraising his improvement (7, 15, 19).

How to Measure Endurance

Endurance is the ability to sustain movement over a long period of time. Endurance depends upon the efficiency of the circulatory and respiratory systems in supplying oxygen to the working muscles and in removing the waste products which are being formed. Muscular strength has a decided influence on endurance, with a strong muscle being able to work over a longer period of time than a weak muscle.

Endurance may be improved by prolonging an activity beyond the point of "comfort." Practice sessions should be regular with the individual continuing to extend the length of each additional session. He must be willing to extend his limits even though he must endure fatigue to do so (7, 11, 19).

Endurance may also be improved by increasing muscular strength, by improving nutrition and general condition and by improving coordination and ability to perform efficiently.

Most persons have developed sufficient endurance for the performance of their daily tasks and unless they are pushed beyond their usual output, they are not aware of having endurance problems. Endurance tests may help an individual recognize his fatigue problems and will help him evaluate improvement as his endurance increases.

Endurance tests are based on the assumption that the person with greater endurance will have the ability to withstand exhaustive work and will return to normal faster than will persons with less endurance. This is usually measured by the heart rate which increases during exercise and returns to normal after exercise. This return to normal is more rapid in individuals who are in good condition than in those who are in poor condition. The individual in good condition can continue work over a longer period of time and can recover from work more rapidly.

The Michigan Pulse Rate Test[8] for physical fitness has been selected for this book because it may be administered to large groups with students scoring for each other. The most difficult part of the test is that of teaching individuals to count their own pulse rate accurately. The test is useful for gross screening of cardiovascular efficiency and will help the individual recognize his endurance needs. The test is interesting to students and requires only a stop watch or a watch with a second hand.

Each student first practices finding and counting his own pulse at rest (sitting). It is necessary for the student to be able to find his pulse quickly and count accurately. Students may check each other for accuracy.

1. The test begins by having each student count his own pulse, at rest, for 15 seconds and record it on the score card.

2. The student runs in place for 15 seconds, lifting the feet 6 inches from the floor at the rate of 3 steps per second. This is running very fast. The student should "push" himself.

3. After running for 15 seconds, the student sits again and counts his own pulse for 15 seconds at the following intervals, while the partner records the results:

> One-half minute after exercise
> One minute after exercise
> Two minutes after exercise
> Three minutes after exercise

[8] "Physical Education in the State of Michigan," *American Physical Education Review*, XXV, April, 1920, pp. 138-39.

4. Rating (time to recover normal pulse rate

$$\frac{1}{2} \text{ minute} \quad \dots\dots\dots\dots \quad \text{fine}$$
$$1 \text{ minute} \quad \dots\dots\dots\dots \quad \text{good}$$
$$2 \text{ minutes} \quad \dots\dots\dots\dots \quad \text{fair}$$
$$3 \text{ minutes} \quad \dots\dots\dots\dots \quad \text{poor}$$

It is important for the test administrator to practice the timing before administering the test. After the initial 15 seconds during which the pulse rate is counted and recorded, the timing breakdown is as follows:

On the signal, "run!" the watch is started.

At the end of:	The action is:
15 seconds	Stop, sit and find pulse
45 seconds	Count
1 minute	Tell score to recorder
1 minute, 15 seconds	Count
1 minute, 30 seconds	Tell score to recorder
2 minutes, 15 seconds	Count
2 minutes, 30 seconds	Tell score to recorder
3 minutes, 15 seconds	Count
3 minutes, 30 seconds	Tell score to recorder

Individual score cards should be used for recording the data and may be set up as follows:

Name_____

Pulse at rest (15 seconds)   _____
Pulse ½ minute after exercise   _____
Pulse 1 minute after exercise   _____
Pulse 2 minutes after exercise   _____
Pulse 3 minutes after exercise   _____

The Larson Cardiovascular Respiratory Rating Scale.   Larson has developed a cardiovascular respiratory rating scale[9] which includes,

[9] Leonard A. Larson, "A Note on Scaling Some Measures of Circulation and Respiration," *Research Quarterly*, 19: 290-95, December, 1948.

among other factors, ratings based on the difference between horizontal and standing pulse rates.

The pulse rate is taken for one minute while the subject is in a horizontal (lying) position. Then the rate is taken for one minute while the subject is in a standing position. The rating on the scale is as follows:

Difference: Standing minus horizontal pulse rates	Rating
0 to 4 beats	Excellent
5 to 11 beats	Very good
12 to 19 beats	Good
20 to 28 beats	Poor
29 to 32 beats	Very poor

The teacher should recognize that these tests give only a gross screening estimate and should not be taken as absolute measures of endurance or vitality. Research studies show that there is great variability among individuals, with pulse rate differences from lying to standing varying from 57 to −15 in healthy individuals.[10] Due to the effect of variations in the emotional state a normal resting pulse may be difficult to obtain.

If the student rates poorly in these tests, however, and also shows other symptoms of fatigue, malaise and general debility, it would be advisable for the teacher to refer him for more extensive examination.

Exercises or procedures used for developing endurance may also be used to evaluate gains or losses in endurance. For example, if the person wishes to develop muscular endurance in the shoulder girdle area, he may chin himself as many times as he can without stopping and on each succeeding day increase the number of chins. The chinning itself may then become the test and as the number of chins increases he may assume that the endurance of the muscle group is increasing.

If running laps is used to improve endurance, increase in the number of laps run and decrease in the time needed for running them may indicate gain in endurance.

How to Appraise Relaxation

"Hypertension" is a condition which affects numerous individuals at one time or another. To alleviate this condition such individuals are

[10] Peter V. Karpovich, *Physiology of Muscular Activity* (Philadelphia: W. B. Saunders Company, 1959), p. 191.

frequently told that they must learn to "relax." Suggestions for relaxing may include (*a*) spending more time in re-creational pursuits, (*b*) obtaining help in resolving problems of everyday living which may be causing undue anxieties or (*c*) understanding the meaning and control of muscle tension.

Appraising relaxation is in reality a test of muscle tension. The process of releasing tension requires an understanding of the "feeling" of tenseness on the part of the individual. Jacobson[11] states: "To become familiar with the experience of tenseness so that it can be recognized wherever it occurs in any portion of the body is highly important in learning to relax." Sensations of tenseness are relatively faint and for that reason they may be overlooked.

Tension may be measured in the following ways:

1. Self-appraisal of tenseness through understanding the "feeling" of tenseness

2. Appraisal of tenseness by a trained observer through manual manipulation of the part of the body

3. Use of the "knee jerk" test

4. Use of electrical measurement by application of electrodes to the muscle

The feeling of tenseness may be identified by inducing tenseness in a muscle and then trying to relax it. Practice in doing this will help the individual distinguish tenseness when it occurs.

Rathbone[12] describes a test "for residual neuromuscular hypertonus" in which a person lies on his back and an operator lifts a body part, such as an arm or leg and determines whether the signs of hypertonus are indicated. These signs are described by Rathbone as "assistance" and "resistance" when the individual assists or resists the operator, "posturing" when the individual maintains the position in which the body part was placed and "perseveration" when the subject continues the motion started by the operator.

The knee jerk test and the electrical measuring device are for the use of the medical doctor in diagnosing tension.

The tests of tension described are subjective with the exception of

---

[11] Edmund Jacobson, *You Must Relax* (New York: McGraw-Hill Book Company, Inc., 1934) p. 70.

[12] Josephine Langworthy Rathbone, *Corrective Physical Education, Third Edition* (Philadelphia: W. B. Saunders Company, 1944) p. 122.

the electrical test; reliability, validity, and objectivity of the tests are not reported. The measuring tools used are the checklist and rating scale for assessing signs of hypertonus.

How to Appraise Skills of Fundamental Movement

Fundamental movement skills include such abilities as running, jumping, throwing, kicking, striking, climbing and catching. Tests which measure these abilities are designated as "motor ability tests."

In selecting a motor ability battery it is important to consider the validating criteria for the battery, since the term "motor ability" has been used to cover a broad area. Some of these tests purport to measure "sensory motor coordination," "agility," and the like with somewhat hazy definitions of these terms. Other motor ability tests propose to measure basic skills and still others, specific sports skills.

Motor ability criteria are as profuse as the wide range of measuring instruments. Some of these criteria are: (a) track and field events; (b) sports skill tests; (c) tests of power and strength; (d) tests of speed and coordination; (e) tests of agility; (f) subjective ratings by juries of experts, observing the subjects in various action situations; (g) previously validated motor ability batteries; (h) composite score of all of the items which constitute the test; (i) tests of endurance, flexibility, strength.

Tests of fundamental skills usually include a measure of running, entailing a shift of weight and position such as is demanded for the change of direction in a shuttle type formation or in an obstacle race. A measure of throwing and jumping is frequently included, and men's batteries usually have a strength factor.

The term "motor educability" is defined in the testing information as the ability of the individual to learn new motor skills. "Motor capacity" is also used in reference to the individual's potentialities in motor development.

Tests of motor educability employ motor problems which are new to the subject. The two tests most frequently used are the Brace Test (2) and the Johnson Test (5). Both of these tests are of a "stunt" type involving performance of new motor patterns in the form of stunts. The Brace test consists of twenty self-testing stunts and was first published in 1927. This test was later revised by McCloy (12) into six groups of ten stunts each, a group for each sex at the high school level, the junior high school level and the upper elementary school level. The McCloy battery is referred to as the "Iowa-Brace."

The Johnson test consists of ten stunts performed on a diagram drawn on a canvas which is placed over two joined mats. Metheney (14) revised the Johnson test, eliminating six of the original items and simplifying the target.

A test which measures achievement in fundamental movement skills plus some aspects of motor educability is the Scott motor ability battery for junior and senior high school girls and college women (20). Five tests were constructed and combined into two batteries, one consisting of three test items and the other of four test items. The validity of the longer battery was R = .91 and the shorter battery, R = .87. The three item battery is described here since it is easier to administer and the difference in validity between the two batteries is negligible. Scott[18] states that the battery is particularly useful for identifying individuals of low achievement in movement areas. She also indicates that the battery has value in predicting rate of achievement in motor areas.

Scott Motor Ability Battery for high school and college women. This battery consists of three items, the obstacle race, the basketball throw for distance, and the standing broad jump.

1. Obstacle Race:

The space needed is 55 feet by 12 feet; equipment needed, three jump standards and a cross bar at least 6 feet long; lines on the floor [*see* Fig. 3-5].

Directions to subject:

Start in a back-lying position on the floor with the heels at line *a*. On the signal, "Ready, Go!" get up and start running toward J. As you come to each square on the floor, step on it with both feet. Run twice around J, turn back to *d*, go under the cross bar, get up on the other side, run to line *c* and continue running between line *b* and *c* until you come to *c* for the third time. The score is the number of seconds (to the nearest one-tenth second) that is required to run the course.

Scott gives suggestions which are helpful to the test administrator.

a. Give instructions to all the class so repetition is not necessary when

[18] M. Gladys Scott and Esther French, *Measurement and Evaluation in Physical Education* (Dubuque, Iowa: William C. Brown Company, Publishers, 1959), pp. 344-56. Quoted by permission.

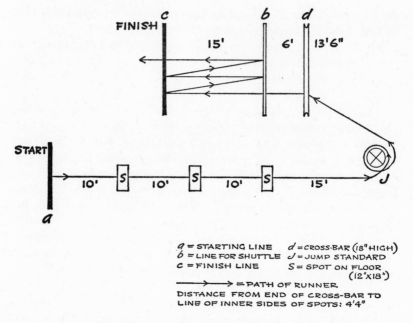

Fig. 3-5. Floor markings for Scott obstacle race.

individuals are ready to run. Demonstrate what is meant by stepping with both feet on each square.

b. Each successive runner should lie down as soon as the girl ahead is up. This avoids delay in starting new runners.

c. If two timers and watches are available, the next girl starts as soon as the one ahead finished circling the standard. Approximately twice the number can be scored on the same course with this arrangement.

d. Do not call the runner back if the toe or heel extends outside of the square. Some feet are too large to fit inside the square if the heel is lowered. Judge performance on whether the stride is adjusted to contact the square and whether there is a transfer of weight from one foot to the other while in the square.

The reliability of this test consisted of a coefficient of .91 obtained on University of Iowa students taking the test on two successive days. The validity of the test was .94 between this test and a longer but similar test. The longer test against which it was compared was validated against several criteria: (a) McCloy total points score consisting of running, throwing and jumping resulted in an r of .65; (b) composite criterion combining the total points, additional sports items and a subjective rating of ability resulted in an r of .58.

2. *Basketball Throw for Distance:*

Space needed is about 80 feet long and 20 feet wide, a throwing line marked about 8 feet from one end of the course and parallel lines every 5 feet beginning 15 feet in front of the throwing line.

Directions to subject:

Start anywhere you wish behind the throwing line, but do not step on or across the line when throwing. Throw in any way you wish, three consecutive times. The score is the distance from the throwing line to the spot where the ball touches the floor. Only the longest throw counts.

Suggestions for the test administrator are as follows:

a. Explain carefully but do not demonstrate. Answer questions about the test except those on throwing technique. If asked whether the throw should be overhand or underhand, whether from a stationary position or with a step or run, simply reply that the throw may be of any type providing the feet are kept behind the line; the purpose is to throw the ball as far as possible. This may not be good teaching procedure, but it is essential for this form of testing if you wish to know how the student is likely to meet similar problems of throwing in a game.

b. It is true that some will profit more than others from seeing other students perform, but they are also the ones who learn quickly from class instruction. The ones who do not profit from errors or success of classmates doubtless will be slow to profit from class instruction.

If the gymnasium is too short and the test cannot be given outside, a diagonal course across the gymnasium may be used. This insures sufficient distance in which to carry on other class activities during the test.

The reliability of this test was r = .89 obtained on successive trials by 200 women at the University of Iowa. Using the same two criteria as described for the obstacle race, the validity coefficients were .79 and .78 respectively for 155 subjects.

3. *Standing Broad Jump:*

If the test is given outside, it is necessary to have a jumping pit with sunken take-off board within 30 inches of the edge of the pit. If given indoors, the test requires mats at least 7½ feet long and a solid board at least 2 feet long (beat boards used with apparatus are excellent) placed against the wall to prevent slipping. If the mat is marked in 2-inch intervals, it eliminates the need to measure each jump with a tape.

Directions to subject:

Stand on the take-off board with feet parallel, toes may be curled over the edge of the board. Take-off from both feet simultaneously; jump as far forward as possible. The score is the distance from the edge of the take-off board to the nearest heel (or to the nearest part of the body if the balance is lost). The best of three trials will be counted.

Suggestions for the test administrator are as follows:

a. Preliminary swinging of arms and flexing of knees are permissible providing the feet are kept in place on the board until the actual take-off.

b. Be sure the performer understands what is to be done. The two-footed take-off is the point most frequently not comprehended from the description.

c. When the use of a take-off board is not feasible, jumping may be done from the mat if the mat is heavy enough that it will not slip.

Reliability of the test on successive trials yielded .79 for 252 women at the University of Iowa and .92 for 144 high school girls. Using the same two criteria as described for the obstacle race, validity coefficients were .79 and .78 respectively for the same 155 subjects.

T-scales for each of the tests and for the battery are shown in Tables 1, 2 and 3. The score for the battery is obtained by averaging the T-scores for the three tests.

Kilday-Latchaw Validation of the Scott Battery used for ninth grade boys. Kilday and Latchaw[14] in a study of ninth grade boys used the Scott three item battery, with slight modifications, as a measure of motor achievement in fundamental movement skills. The battery was successful with these particular subjects in that the students were interested in the tests, and the range of scores indicated that it was of suitable difficulty for these subjects. The tests were administered in an outdoor area on a blacktop surface. Mats were used for the broad jump.

Further study is needed to determine the value of these tests in measuring achievement in fundamental movement skills for boys of secondary school age. Although achievement scales were constructed for these particular subjects, they are not presented because of the limited size of the sample. It is recommended that each school develop T-scales for their own students.

[14] Kenneth Kilday and Marjorie Latchaw, *Study of Motor Ability in Ninth Grade Boys* (Unpublished Studies, University of California, Los Angeles, 1961.)

TABLE 1.

T-Scales for Motor Ability Tests for High School Girls
Scott Motor Ability Battery

T-Score	Basketball Throw (feet)	Broad Jump (inches)	Obstacle Race (seconds)	T-Score
80	71			80
79		96		79
78				78
77	68	94		77
76	66		18.5-18.9	76
75	65			75
74	64	92		74
73	63			73
72	61			72
71	59	90		71
70	55	88	19.0-19.4	70
69	54			69
68	52	86		68
67	51		19.5-19.9	67
66	50			66
65	49			65
64	48	84	20.0-20.4	64
63	47			63
62	46	82	20.5-20.9	62
61		80		61
60	45			60
59	44	78	21.0-21.4	59
58	43			58
57	42	76	21.5-21.9	57
56	41			56
55	40	74		55
54			22.0-22.4	54
53	39			53
52		72		52
51	37		22.5-22.9	51
50	36			50
49	35	70		49
48		68	23.0-23.4	48
47	34	66		47
46	33		23.5-23.9	46
45	32	64		45

From Scott and French, *Measurement and Evaluation in Physical Education.*

TABLE 1. (Continued)

T-Score	Basketball Throw (feet)	Broad Jump (inches)	Obstacle Race (seconds)	T-Score
44	31		24.0-24.4	44
43		62		43
42	30		24.5-24.9	42
41	29	60		41
40	28			40
39		58	25.0-25.4	39
38	27	56		38
37		54	25.5-25.9	37
36	26		26.0-26.4	36
35		52	26.5-26.9	35
34	25	50	27.0-27.4	34
33				33
32	24	47	27.5-27.9	32
31	23			31
30		44	28.0-28.4	30
29	22		28.5-28.9	29
28			29.0-29.4	28
27	21		29.5-29.9	27
26		40	30.0-30.4	26
25	20			25
24			30.5-31.4	24
23	19	36	31.5-32.4	23
22			32.5-34.9	22
21	16			21
20			35.0-36.0	20

A battery score may be computed by averaging the T-scores for all three tests.

1. Basketball Throw for Distance:

Space needed is approximately 150 feet long and 20 feet wide. A throwing line is marked 10 feet from one end of the course. Parallel lines are marked every 5 feet, beginning 15 feet in front of the throwing line.

Directions to subject:

Start anywhere you wish behind the throwing line and throw in any way you wish, but don't step across the line when throwing. You have three trials. The score for each trial is the distance in feet from the throwing line to the place where the ball touches the ground. Your score for this test is the best of three trials.

Suggestions for administering the test are on pages 76-77.

TABLE 2.

T-Scales for Motor Ability Tests for College Women
Scott Motor Ability Battery

T-Score	Basketball Throw (feet)	Broad Jump (inches)	Obstacle Race (seconds)	T-Score
85	75	86	17.5-17.9	85
84				84
83	71		18.0-18.4	83
82				82
81		85		81
80	70			80
79	69		18.5-18.9	79
78	68	84		78
77	67	83		77
76	66			76
75	65	82	19.0-19.4	75
74	64	81		74
73	62	80		73
72	61	79	19.5-19.9	72
71	59			71
70	58	78	20.0-20.4	70
69	57	77		69
68	56	76		68
67	55	75	20.5-20.9	67
66	54	74		66
65	52			65
64	51	73	21.0-21.4	64
63	50	72		63
62	48	71	21.5-21.9	62
61	47			61
60	46	70		60
59	45	69	22.0-22.4	59
58	44	68		58
57	43	67	22.5-22.9	57
56	42			56
55	41	66	23.0-23.4	55
54	40	65		54
53	39	64	23.5-23.9	53
52	38	63		52
51	37		24.0-24.4	51

From Scott and French, *Measurement and Evaluation in Physical Education.*

TABLE 2. (Continued)

50	36	62		50
49	35	61	24.5-24.9	49
48		60		48
47	34	59	25.0-25.4	47
46	33	58		46
45	32	57	25.5-25.9	45
44	31			44
43		56	26.0-26.4	43
42	30	55		42
41		54	26.5-26.9	41
40	29	53	27.0-27.4	40
39	28	52		39
38			27.5-27.9	38
37	27	51	28.0-28.4	37
36	26	50		36
35		49	28.5-28.9	35
34	25	48	29.0-29.4	34
33		47	29.5-29.9	33
32		46	30.0-30.4	32
31		45	30.5-30.9	31
30	24	44	31.0-31.4	30
29		43	31.5-31.9	29
28	23	42	32.0-32.4	28
27	21	41	32.5-32.9	27
26		40	33.0-33.4	26
25	20	39	33.5-33.9	25
24		38	34.0-34.4	24
23		37	34.5-34.9	23
22		36		22
21	19		35.0-35.4	21
20				20
19		35	35.5-35.9	19
18				18
17	18			17
16				16
15				15
14			43.5-43.9	14
13		30	45.5-45.9	13

A battery score may be computed by averaging the T-scores for all three tests.

TABLE 3.

T-Scales for Motor Ability Battery for Physical Education Major Students (Women)
Scott Motor Ability Battery

The battery score is computed by the formula: 2.0 basketball throw (feet) + 1.4 broad jump (inches) — 1.0 obstacles race (seconds).

T-Score	Battery Score	T-Score	T-Score	Battery Score	T-Score
80	228	80	50	160	50
79		79	49	156	49
78	226	78	48	154	48
77		77	47	152	47
76		76	46	150	46
75		75	45	146	45
74	224	74	44	142	44
73	222	73	43	140	43
72	220	72	42	138	42
71	218	71	41	136	41
70	216	70	40	134	40
69	214	69	39	132	39
68		68	38	128	38
67	212	67	37	126	37
66	210	66	36	122	36
65	206	65	35	120	35
64	202	64	34	116	34
63	200	63	33	114	33
62	198	62	32	112	32
61	194	61	31		31
60	192	60	30	110	30
59	188	59	29		29
58	186	58	28	108	28
57	184	57	27	104	27
56	180	56	26		26
55	176	55	25		25
54	172	54	24	96	24
53	170	53	23		23
52	166	52	22		22
51	162	51	21	92	21

From Scott and French, *Measurement and Evaluation in Physical Education.*

a. Measure each trial from the throwing line to the spot where the ball touches the floor, estimating to the nearest foot.

b. The test should be explained verbally but should not be demonstrated. Avoid giving any suggestions or instruction on how to throw the ball. If questions are asked concerning how the ball may be thrown, tell subjects that ball may be thrown in any way providing the feet are kept back of the throwing line. If a subject throws from a run or from a stationary position, either is acceptable.

c. The test may be administered either in the gymnasium or on the field. If administered in the gymnasium, it may be necessary to draw a diagonal course across the room, which leaves little space for carrying on any other type of activity. Wind conditions may be a problem if the test is administered on the field. Testing should be done when wind is at a minimum.

The reliability of this test obtained from successive administrations of the test resulted in .891 for 37 subjects. The test was validated against a composite of judges' ratings of general over-all ability in physical education activities and combined T-score of strength measures, including push-ups, chins, jump and reach. The coefficients were .622 and .687 respectively.

2. *Obstacle Race:*

Space needed is 60 feet by 15 feet, marked as indicated in Figure 3-5. The equipment needed consists of three jump standards, a cross bar at least 8 feet long and a stop watch calibrated in tenths of a second.

Directions to subject:

Lie on your back on the floor with your heels on the starting line. On the signal, "Ready, Go!" get up and run toward the first rectangle on the floor. Step on the rectangle with both feet and continue on to the next two rectangles. Be sure that you step in each rectangle with both feet. Run completely around the jump standard as indicated by the arrow on the floor, starting around the outside. Go under the cross bar toward the finish line. Touch the finish line with your foot, run back to line b, and continue running from one line to the other until your foot touches the finish line for the third time. Your score is the number of seconds to the nearest one-tenth second that it takes you to run the course.

Suggestions which may be helpful to the test administrator are as follows:

a. Subject should be in back-lying position.

b. Give verbal explanation of the test. Demonstrate *only* what is meant by stepping in the rectangle with both feet (there must be a transfer of weight from one foot to the other while in the rectangle.) If toe or heel extends outside of rectangle, do not call the runner back.

c. If a subject makes an error in executing any part of the course, call him back and after a brief rest, have him run it again.

The reliability of this test obtained from successive administrations of the test resulted in .889. Using the same criteria for validation as described for the basketball throw for distance, the coefficients were .553 and .580 respectively.

3. *Standing Broad Jump:*
Test may be given outside or in the gymnasium. If a jumping pit is used, it should have a sunken take-off board within 30 inches of the edge of the pit. If a mat is used, it should be at least 7½ feet long with a solid board at least 2 feet long for a take-off board. A calibrated mat facilitates scoring since it eliminates the measuring of each jump with the tape. If steel tapes are available, they may be fastened on either side of the mat with safety pins and tape. They should be constantly checked to be sure they have not become dislodged during the jumps.

Directions to subject:
Stand on the take-off board with toes curled over the edge of the board. Take off from both feet simultaneously. Jump as far forward as possible. The score is the distance from the edge of the board to the nearest contact made on landing. This is usually to the nearest heel, but if you lose your balance and fall backward, it is measured to the part of your body nearest the take-off board. You have three trials and your score will be the best of the three trials.

Suggestions for the test administrator are as follows:
a. Measure each jump to the nearest inch from the edge of the take-off board to the nearest part of the body contacting the mat or to the nearest mark in the pit. If a take-off board is difficult or impossible to provide, jumping may be done from the mat if it is heavy enough to prevent slipping.

b. Preliminary swinging of arms and flexing of knees is permitted as long as the feet are kept in place on the board until the take-off. Do not demonstrate but be sure the subject understands that the take-off must be from both feet simultaneously.

The reliability of this test obtained on successive trials was .825. Using the same criteria for validation as described for the basketball throw for distance, the coefficients were .518, and .687 respectively.

Larson (8) experimented with 33 tests and test variables selected to measure fundamental motor ability which resulted in two test batteries, one for outdoor testing and the other for indoor testing. The batteries were validated against a criterion of 25 motor ability items with a multiple correlation of .97 for the indoor test and .98 for the outdoor test. Both batteries are described here and achievement scales for college men are included.

Larson General Motor Ability Test for College Men. The indoor test[15] consists of the dodging run, bar snap, chinning, dips and vertical jump. The outdoor test has the baseball throw for distance, chinning, bar snap and vertical jump.

1. Indoor Test:

a. DODGING RUN. Five parallel lanes are constructed, 3 feet wide and 11 yards long. Five low hurdles or some other object of similar nature are placed in the first, second, fourth, third and fifth lanes (see Fig. 3-6). The runner starts at the starting point and runs as

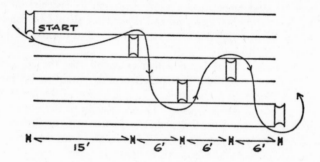

Fig. 3-6. Larson's dodging run.

indicated by the curved line. The time necessary for *two complete* runs is the score. Regulation gymnasium equipment should be used. The subject should not touch the hurdles when circling them.

b. BAR SNAP. The horizontal bar is placed at 4½ feet. Mats should be placed on floor for landing. The subject stands close to the bar, grasping it, then swings underneath shooting the feet close to the bar and upward. The back should be arched, and the subject should drop the bar when sufficient height has been reached for the best distance. The distance from the plane of the horizontal bar to the maximum distance (back heels) is the score (three trials). Practice should be allowed so as to develop the skill necessary for this test. The subject is

[15] Leonard A. Larson and Rachael D. Yocom, *Measurement and Evaluation in Physical, Health, and Recreation Education* (St. Louis: The C. V. Mosby Company, 1951), pp. 487-89. Quoted by permission.

not allowed to jump before the underswing, but must start with feet on the floor.

c. CHINNING. Use horizontal bar at such height that subject's feet do not touch the floor when subject is in lowered position. Subject can use either the forward or reverse grip. To begin, the subject hangs from the bar, then pulls himself up until his chin is over the bar, then lowers himself until arms are straight. The subject is not permitted to kick, to swing, or to rest. Partial chins do not count. The count is one for each full chin.

d. DIPS (ten minute rest between dips and chinning). The subject jumps to an arm rest position at the end of the parallel bars (bars at shoulder height), with arms fully extended. From this position the subject lowers his body to a right angle arm bend position and pushes up to the first position. The subject is not permitted to rest in any position, to swing or to kick. Partial dips do not count. The count is one for the jump into the first position, then one for each full dip.

e. VERTICAL JUMP. The preferred equipment for the measurement of the vertical jump is the MacCurdy Vertical Jump-meter. If this equipment is not available the well known jump-and-reach method is used. A blackboard or cloth is placed on the wall high enough to record the reach and the best jump. The subject is asked to stand as close to the wall (face toward wall) as possible with both arms upstretched, with feet flat on the floor. A chalk mark is made of this maximum reach at tip of fingers for each hand. A line is then drawn between the two points. The subject then stands sideways with right or left arm close to the wall. Chalk dust is placed on the middle finger. The subject jumps, throwing both arms upward, recording height with the hand near the wall. The difference between maximum reach and maximum jump is recorded to the nearest half-inch. The best one of three trials is selected.

2. *Outdoor Test:*

a. BASEBALL THROW FOR DISTANCE. A twelve-inch inseam ball is used. The subject is allowed to run to the throwing line, but must not overstep the line. The field is marked at five-foot intervals to facilitate measurement. The examiner estimates the distance between markers when the ball hits the ground. A warm-up period should be allowed and the best throw of three trials selected for the score. The measurement is recorded in feet.

b. CHINNING. See directions for indoor test.

c. BAR SNAP. See directions for indoor test.

d. VERTICAL JUMP. See directions for indoor test.

Achievement scales for each of the tests are shown in Table 4.

TABLE 4.

Scoring Tables for the Larson General Motor Ability Tests for College Men

Indoor Test

Directions for using table:
1. Change raw scores into weighted T-scores.
2. Sum the weighted T-scores to obtain "index score."
3. Determine classification as follows:

Index Score	Classification
630-up	Excellent
558-629	Good
486-557	Average
414-485	Poor
413-down	Very poor

DODGING RUN		BAR SNAP		DIPPING		CHINNING		VERTICAL JUMP	
Raw Score	Wtd. T-Score	Raw Score	Wtd. T-Score	Raw Score	Wtd. T-Score	Raw Score	Wtd. T-Score	Raw Score	Wtd. T-Score
(Sec.)		(Ins.)		(No.)		(No.)		(Ins.)	
28.0	29	102	324	23	128	23	218	26.0	78
27.8	31	101	321	22	125	22	213	25.5	76
27.6	32	100	319	21	122	21	210	25.0	74
27.4	33	99	316	20	117	20	207	24.5	72
27.2	35	98	313	19	114	19	205	24.0	70
27.0	36	97	311	18	112	18	199	23.5	68
26.8	37	96	308	17	110	17	194	23.0	66
26.6	38	95	306	16	107	16	188	22.5	64
26.4	39	94	304	15	102	15	183	22.0	62
26.2	40	93	302	14	99	14	177	21.5	61
26.0	41	92	300	13	96	13	172	21.0	59
25.8	42	91	298	12	93	12	164	20.5	58
26.6	43	90	296	11	90	11	158	20.0	56
25.4	44	89	294	10	86	10	150	19.5	54
25.2	45	88	292	9	83	9	142	19.0	52
25.0	46	87	290	8	80	8	137	18.5	51
24.8	47	86	288	7	75	7	131	18.0	49
24.6	48	85	286	6	72	6	123	17.5	47
24.4	48	84	284	5	69	5	115	17.0	45
24.2	49	83	281	4	66	4	109	16.5	44
24.0	50	82	279	3	61	3	101	16.0	42
23.8	51	81	277	2	56	2	93	15.5	40
23.6	53	80	275	1	48	1	48	15.0	38
23.4	54	79	273	0	38	0	74	14.5	37
23.2	55	78	271					14.0	35
23.0	57	77	269					13.5	33
22.8	58	76	267					13.0	31
22.6	59	75	265					12.5	29

TABLE 4. (Continued)

DODGING RUN		BAR SNAP		DIPPING		CHINNING		VERTICAL JUMP	
Raw Score	Wtd. T-Score	Raw Score	Wtd. T-Score	Raw Score	Wtd. T-Score	Raw Score	Wtd. T-Score	Raw Score	Wtd. T-Score
(Sec.)		(Ins.)		(No.)		(No.)		(Ins.)	
22.4	61	74	263					12.0	27
22.2	62	73	261					11.5	26
22.0	63	72	259					11.0	24
21.8	65	71	256						
21.6	66	70	254						
21.4	67	69	251						
21.2	68	68	248						
21.0	70	67	246						
20.8	71	66	240						
20.6	73	65	240						
20.4	74	64	238						
20.2	76	63	235						
20.0	77	62	232						
19.8	79	61	230						
19.6	80	60	227						
19.4	81	59	224						
19.2	83	58	222						
19.0	84	57	219						
		56	216						
		55	213						
		54	210						
		53	207						
		52	204						
		51	200						
		50	197						
		49	194						
		48	190						
		47	186						
		46	182						
		45	178						
		44	174						
		43	170						
		42	166						
		41	161						
		40	155						
		39	150						
		38	145						
		37	139						
		36	134						
		35	128						
		34	122						
		33	115						
		32	109						
		31	103						
		30	97						

TABLE 4. (Continued)

Outdoor Test

Directions for using table:
1. Change raw scores into weighted T-scores.
2. Sum the weighted T-scores to obtain "index score."
3. Determine classification as follows:

Index Score	Classification
728-up	Excellent
642-727	Good
556-641	Average
470-555	Poor
469-down	Very poor

BASEBALL THROW				CHINNING		BAR SNAP		VERTICAL JUMP	
Raw Score	Wtd. T-Score	Raw Score	Wtd. T-Score	Raw Score	Wtd. T-Score	Raw Score	Wtd. T-Score	Raw Score	Wtd. T-Score
(Feet)		(Feet)		(No.)		(Ins.)		(Ins.)	
270	178	250	172	23	293	102	393	26.0	78
268	178	248	169	22	285	101	389	25.5	76
266	177	246	167	21	282	100	386	25.0	74
264	176	244	165	20	278	99	383	24.5	72
262	175	242	163	19	275	98	380	24.0	70
260	174	240	161	18	267	97	377	23.5	68
258	173	238	159	17	260	96	373	23.0	66
256	173	236	157	16	253	95	371	22.5	64
254	173	234	155	15	245	94	368	22.0	62
252	172	232	153	14	238	93	366	21.5	61
230	152	150	91	13	231	92	363	21.0	59
228	150	148	90	12	220	91	361	20.5	58
226	148	146	89	11	212	90	358	20.0	56
224	146	144	87	10	201	89	356	19.5	54
222	145	142	86	9	199	88	354	19.0	52
220	143	140	85	8	183	87	351	18.5	51
218	141	138	83	7	176	86	349	18.0	49
216	139	136	82	6	165	85	346	17.5	47
214	137	134	81	5	154	84	344	17.0	45
212	136	132	79	4	146	83	341	16.5	44
210	134	130	78	3	135	82	339	16.0	42
208	133	128	77	2	124	81	336	15.5	40
206	132	126	75	1	117	80	334	15.0	38
204	131	124	74	0	99	79	331	14.5	37
202	130	122	73			78	329	14.0	35
200	129	120	71			77	327	13.5	33
198	128	118	70			76	324	13.0	31
196	127	116	70			75	322	12.5	29
194	125	114	69			74	319	12.0	27
192	124	112	68			73	317	11.5	26

TABLE 4. (Continued)

BASEBALL THROW				CHINNING		BAR SNAP		VERTICAL JUMP	
Raw Score	Wtd. T-Score	Raw Score	Wtd. T-Score	Raw Score	Wtd. T-Score	Raw Score	Wtd. T-Score	Raw Score	Wtd. T-Score
(Feet)		(Feet)		(No.)		(Ins.)		(Ins.)	
190	123	110	67			72	314	11.0	24
188	121	108	66			71	311		
186	119	106	65			70	308		
184	117	104	64			69	304		
182	116	102	63			68	301		
180	114	100	62			67	298		
178	112	98	61			66	295		
176	110	96	60			65	291		
174	108	94	58			64	288		
172	107	92	57			63	285		
170	105	90	56			62	281		
168	103	88	55			61	278		
166	102	86	55			60	275		
164	101	84	54			59	272		
162	99	82	54			58	269		
160	98	80	54			57	265		
158	97	78	51			56	262		
156	95	76	49			55	259		
154	94	74	47			54	255		
152	93	72	45			53	251		
		70	42			52	247		
						51	243		
						50	239		
						49	235		
						48	231		
						47	226		
						46	221		
						45	216		
						44	211		
						43	206		
						42	201		
						41	195		
						40	188		
						39	182		
						38	175		
						37	168		
						36	162		
						35	155		
						34	147		
						33	140		
						32	133		
						31	125		
						30	118		

Latchaw (10) constructed seven tests to measure general motor achievement of fourth, fifth and sixth grade boys and girls. Test reliability was determined for each grade level and for each sex. Internal validity was used for each test; that is, the test purported to measure only the particular performance that constituted the test. Achievement scales were computed for each test and each sex at each grade level.

Relationship between age, height and weight factors and test performance was low, and achievement scales were constructed without using regression equations for age, height and weight.

Latchaw Motor Achievement Tests for Fourth, Fifth and Sixth Grade Boys and Girls. Seven tests are included in this battery:[16] (1) basketball wall pass; (2) volleyball wall volley; (3) vertical jump; (4) standing broad jump; (5) shuttle run; (6) soccer wall volley; (7) softball repeated throws.

1. *Basketball Wall Pass:* [see Fig. 3-7]

On a flat wall space, mark a rectangle eight feet wide and four feet high, at a distance of three feet from the floor. A restraining line eight feet long is drawn on the floor four feet from the wall and parallel to

[16] M. Gladys Scott and Esther French, *Measurement and Evaluation in Physical Education* (Dubuque, Iowa: William C. Brown Company, Publishers, 1959), pp. 364-385. By permission.

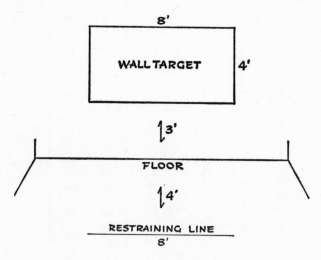

Fig. 3-7. Markings for basketball wall pass.

the wall target. Equipment needed consists of a regulation basketball and a stop watch.

Test directions:

The subject stands at any place he chooses back of the restraining line. On the signal "Go!" he throws the ball against the wall into the target area in any manner that he chooses, and continues successive throws until the signal "Stop!" is given. If the ball gets out of control at any time, he must recover it himself without assistance. A successful throw is one that goes into the target area and is made from behind the restraining line. Line balls are not fair hits. The ball may be caught on a bounce if the subject so chooses. However, the ball need not be caught to constitute a successful throw.

A ten-second practice trial is given while the test administrator scores verbally, encouraging the subject to retrieve lost balls rapidly, and to throw the ball as fast as he can successfully manipulate it. This score is not recorded.

One point is given for each successful throw. Two fifteen-second trials are given after the practice trial. The total number of points is recorded for each trial. The better of the two trials is the final score for the test.

Suggestions for the test administrator:

a. One administrator can time and score approximately 50 subjects in one hour. If several testing areas and additional scorers are available, the tests may be given very quickly. It is possible that the children could score for each other if they were given an opportunity to practice with the teacher beforehand.

b. It is important that the administrator demonstrate the test while he is explaining it to the subjects.

Reliability coefficients for this test were as follows: (a) for boys: grade 4 = .91, grade 5 = .84, grade 6 = .78; (b) for girls: grade 4 = .94, grade 5 = .89, grade 6 = .83.

2. *Volleyball Wall Volley:* [see Fig. 3-8]

On a flat wall space, mark a rectangle eight feet wide and at least four feet high, at a distance of three feet from the floor. A restraining line eight feet long is drawn on the floor four feet from the wall and parallel to the wall target. Equipment needed is a regulation volleyball and a stop watch.

Test directions:

The subject stands at any position he chooses in back of the restraining line. On the signal "Go!" he tosses or throws the ball against the wall into the target area, and as it rebounds he continues to bat it repeatedly against the wall. The ball may be tossed against the wall

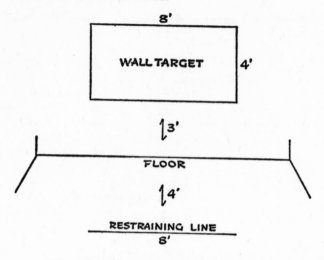

Fig. 3-8. Markings for volleyball wall volley.

when it is necessary to start it again. If the ball gets out of control, the subject retrieves it himself, brings it back to the restraining line and starts it again. A successful hit is one that, upon rebounding from the wall, is clearly *batted* into the target area from behind the restraining line on the floor. If the ball is thrown or pushed against the wall, it does not constitute a successful hit. Line balls are not fair hits.

The subject is given a ten-second practice trial. The test administrator scores verbally during this trial, calling the attention of the subject to balls that are not legal hits if he pushes the ball at any time. This score is not recorded.

One point is given for each successful hit. Four fifteen second trials are given after the practice trial. The total number of points is recorded for each trial. The best of the four trials is the final score for the test.

Suggestions for the test administrator:

a. One administrator can time and score approximately 30 subjects in one hour if the subjects have had previous experience in volleyball. Inexperienced subjects need more instruction in batting and are frequently unsuccessful during the practice trial. When this is the case, the administrator should demonstrate proper hitting before each of the test trials, or until the subject is able to execute a correct hit. If the subject is unable to execute a correct hit throughout his four trials, his score for each trial will be zero, and his score for the test will be zero. This test is too difficult for children to score unless they have had considerable experience in judging a clearly batted ball.

b. It is important that the administrator first demonstrate this test for the subjects being tested, being careful to distinguish clearly between a batted ball, a thrown ball, and a pushed ball.

Reliability coefficients for this test were as follows: (a) for boys: grade 4 = .85, grade 5 = .89, grade 6 = .91; (b) for girls: grade 4 = .88, grade 5 = .92, grade 6 = .93.

3. Vertical Jump:

One-inch cloth strips are suspended from a horizontal bar and spaced at one inch intervals from each other. The longest strip is five feet from the floor and the shortest strip is eight feet eleven inches from the floor. Each strip is weighted with a penny at the end nearest the floor to insure even hanging.

Test directions:

The subject stands with both heels on the floor under the suspended strips and reaching with one hand, touches the highest strip that he can. This is recorded under "reaching height." The subject jumps from a stationary position under the bar and reaches the highest strip that he can. He may start from a crouch if he wishes but he may not take any steps or preliminary bounces. Any number of trials is allowed, but it is advisable to estimate the approximate place along the scale where the subject's best jump will be in order to avoid fatigue from too many trials.

The score is the difference in inches between the height of the reach and the height of the best jump.

Suggestions for the test administrator:

a. When reaching height is taken, the subject is encouraged to stretch as far as he can, being sure that both heels are on the floor. If the subject is reaching at his maximum height, the reaching shoulder will be higher than the other shoulder.

b. Portable equipment was devised for this study to facilitate use in a number of schools. Two nine-foot uprights, 2½ inches by 1⅛ inches were hinged to a nine-foot crossbar of the same dimensions. The crossbar was itself hinged in the center. The hubs of the hinges were countersunk and reversed. The brad was removed from the regular hinge and a bolt with a wing nut was used to give stability and still allow the hinge to fold. Each upright and half of the crossbar could be folded compactly into four ½ foot lengths. For the base, two 2 x 4 pieces 2 feet in length were set on edge. A space 1⅞ inches by 1 inch was left in which to insert the uprights. Sixteen inch 2 x 4 crossbars were laid flat to give additional strength to the base. The cloth strips were tacked to the horizontal bar in the manner previously described.

c. If it is not feasible to make such jumping equipment and if a MacCurdy Vertical Jumpmeter is not available, the jump-and-reach method against the wall may be used. The subject faces the wall, both heels on the floor, and reaches as high as possible with one hand. A chalk mark is made at the reaching height. The subject then stands sideways, chalk dust or water is placed on his middle finger, and he jumps, touching the wall at the height of the jump. Three trials are allowed, and the score is the best of the three trials. The score is the difference in inches between the height of the reach and the height of the jump.

d. One administrator can test approximately 40 subjects in one hour. As the administrator becomes experienced in estimating the approximate height the subject will jump, the number of trials per subject may be cut down considerably, which in turn decreases the testing time.

Reliability coefficients for this test were as follows: (a) for boys: grade 4 = .90, grade 5 = .92, grade 6 = .93; (b) for girls: grade 4 = .92, grade 5 = .95, grade 6 = .95.

4. Standing Broad Jump:

Equipment needed includes a tumbling mat at least nine feet long, and a measuring tape unless the mat is calibrated permanently.

Test directions:

The subject stands with both toes touching the restraining line that marks the take-off area, and from this standing position jumps as far forward as he can. Any preliminary movement that is made must be executed with some part of both feet in contact with the take-off area. The subject is given three successive trials and measurement is taken to the last inch. For example, if the subject jumps five feet, two and one-half inches, the jump is recorded as five feet, two inches. This distance is measured from the restraining line of the take-off area to the nearest contact made on landing. (This is usually to the first heel mark made on landing, but if the subject loses balance, falls backward and catches himself with his hand or body, the mark nearest the restraining line is used in measuring the distance of the jump.) The best of three trials in feet and inches is the score for the test.

Suggestions to test administrator:

a. It is important to check the position of the feet of each subject, making sure that the toes are not over the restraining line. If any preliminary bounce or spring is taken in which one or both feet leave the surface of the take-off area, the jump is not legal and a score of zero is recorded. It is advisable to encourage the subject to throw his weight forward if he feels himself losing balance upon landing; if he falls backward, the distance of his jump is considerably shortened.

b. If a mat is used rather than a jumping pit, the restraining line should be marked on the mat, rather than on the floor, and far enough from the end of the mat to allow the entire surface of both feet to rest comfortably on the mat. If an outdoor jumping pit is used, a stable surface for the take-off area must be provided. All subjects in this particular study were measured on a mat.

c. A mat may be calibrated by using India ink, or a measuring tape may be fastened to one side of the mat with pins or tape. This will facilitate speed and accuracy in measuring. If these methods are used, one administrator can test between 40 and 50 subjects in one hour.

Reliability coefficients for this test were as follows: (*a*) for boys: grade 4 = .97, grade 5 = .94, grade 6 = .94; (*b*) for girls: grade 4 = .93, grade 5 = .97, grade 6 = .86.

5. *Shuttle Run:* [*see* Fig. 3-9]

Two 12-inch lines are marked on the floor, parallel to each other and at a distance of 20 feet apart. The line that is indicated to be the

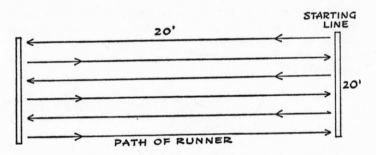

Fig. 3-9. Markings for shuttle run.

starting line should have an area in back of it free from obstruction that is at least 20 feet long, to give the runner an opportunity to check his speed *after* passing this line upon completing his run. Equipment needed is a stop watch calibrated in one-tenth seconds.

Test directions:

The subject stands with the toe of his forward foot on the starting line. On the signal "Go!" he runs to the opposite line, touches it (or beyond it) with one or both feet and returns to the starting line. The subject does not stop, but continues running to the opposite line until he has completed three trips, or a total of 120 feet. If the subject fails to touch, or step over, a line at any time during the run, he is stopped at once and no score is recorded for the trial. After a brief resting period, he is given one opportunity to repeat this performance, and if he fails again to execute the test correctly, a score of zero is recorded for the trial. The time in one-tenth seconds is taken from the signal "Go!" to the crossing of the starting line upon completing the three trips (120 feet). Two trials are given in this test. Subjects are tested in pairs, with one of the pair resting while the other is performing, thus alternating with each other on the trials. The score for this test is the better of the two trials, recorded in seconds to the nearest tenth.

Suggestions for the test administrator:

a. This test should be demonstrated and explained carefully, thus avoiding the necessity of a practice trial on the part of the subject, as his best score is frequently made on his initial performance.

b. The subject should be encouraged to run across the starting line (which is also the finish line) at full speed upon the completion of his third trip in order that he may make the best possible score. Gymnasium shoes are necessary for executing this test; street shoes or stockings present too many difficulties for the quick turns that are necessary in this test.

c. If a number of subjects are to be tested, chalk is not practical for the floor markings because it rubs off too easily; white tempera paint (washable) is recommended.

d. One administrator can test between 40 and 50 subjects in one hour.

Reliability coefficients for this test were as follows: (a) for boys: grade 4 = .89, grade 5 = .89, grade 6 = .89; (b) for girls: grade 4 = .84, grade 5 = .85, grade 6 = .79.

6. *Soccer Wall Volley:* [*see* Fig. 3-10]

On a flat wall space mark a rectangle four feet wide and two and one-half feet from the floor. A similar area is marked on the floor, four feet wide and two and one-half feet from the wall target, parallel to the wall target. The four foot line on the floor farthest from the wall target is extended one foot on either side and constitutes the restraining line (six feet long.) Equipment needed includes a regulation soccer ball and a stop watch.

Test directions:

The ball is placed back of the restraining lines at any position desired by the subject (usually toward the center of the line). On the signal "Go!" the subject kicks the ball against the wall into the target area, and as it rebounds he continues to kick it repeatedly against the wall. If the ball gets out of control, the subject retrieves it himself, brings it back to the restraining line and starts it again. The subject may not touch the ball with his hands while it is in the rectangular

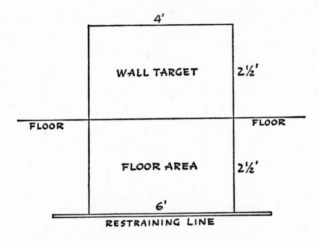

Fig. 3-10. Markings for soccer wall volley.

floor area between the restraining line and the target (the kicking area). If the ball stops within this area, he must move it by using his foot. At any time that the ball is outside of this rectangular floor area, the subject may use his hands in retrieving or moving the ball. A successful hit is one that is kicked with the foot into the target area on the wall from *behind* the restraining line on the floor. Line balls are not fair hits. To constitute a fair hit, the ball must be kicked from in back of the restraining line (not *on* it) and must land between the lines that bound the wall target. The subject is given a fifteen-second practice trial. The test administrator scores verbally during this trial, calling attention to balls that are not legal hits. This score is not recorded. One point is given for each successful hit. Each time that the ball is touched with the hands when it is inside the rectangular floor area, one point is subtracted from the score. Four fifteen-second trials are given, after the practice trial. The total number of points is recorded for *each* trial. The best of the four trials is the final score for the test.

Suggestions for the test administrator:

a. One administrator can time and score between 25 and 30 subjects in one hour, if the group has had no previous experience in kicking a soccer ball. Inexperienced subjects need more instruction in kicking the ball without raising it above the target and are frequently unsuccessful during the practice trial, necessitating further demonstration and explanation by the administrator.

b. When a number of subjects are being tested, all floor markings should be made with white tempera paint in place of chalk.

Reliability coefficients for this test were as follows: (*a*) for boys: grade 4 = .82, grade 5 = .89, grade 6 = .88; (*b*) for girls: grade 4 = .77, grade 5 = .83, grade 6 = .77.

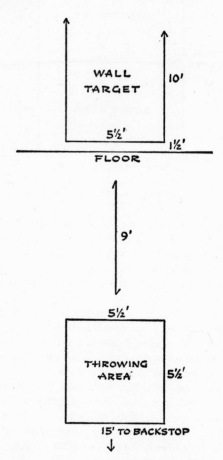

Fig. 3-11. Markings for softball repeated throws.

7. *Softball Repeated Throws:* [*see* Fig. 3-11]

On a flat wall space, mark a target area five and one-half feet wide and at least ten feet high, at a distance of one-half foot from the floor. A throwing area, five and one-half feet square is marked on the floor at a distance of nine feet from the target and parallel to it. A backstop, twelve feet long and two and one-half feet high (at least) is placed fifteen feet in back of the throwing area. Equipment needed includes a twelve-inch inseam softball and a stop watch.

Test directions:

The subject stands at any place he chooses inside of the throwing area. On the signal "Go!" he throws the ball against the wall into the target area, using an overhand throw, and continues successive throws until the signal "Stop!" is given. The balls may be received from the target either on the bounce or on the fly. If the ball gets out of control at any time, the subject must recover it himself without assistance. Most of these balls will be stopped by the backstop, but if this is not the case, the subject must chase the balls himself. A successful throw is one that is an *overhand* throw that goes into the target area and is made from inside the throwing area. Line balls are not fair hits. The subject is given a ten-second practice trial. The test administrator scores verbally during this trial. This score is not recorded. One point is given for each successful throw. Two fifteen-second trials are given after the practice trial. The total number of points is recorded for *each* trial. The better of the two trials is the final score for the test.

Suggestions for the test administrator:

a. One administrator can time and score approximately 50 subjects in one hour. If other testing areas and scorers are available, the test may be given very quickly.

b. A backstop may be readily devised by using an ordinary table and turning it on its side, with the table surface facing the target.

c. If a number of subjects are to be tested, white tempera paint is recommended for all markings.

Reliability coefficients for this test were as follows: (*a*) for boys: grade 4 = .82, grade 5 = .11, grade 6 = .85; (*b*) for girls: grade 4 = .80, grade 5 = .82, grade 6 = .85.

Achievement scales for boys and girls at each grade level are presented in Tables 5 through 11.

Other tests of fundamental movement which are reported in the testing literature include:

1. Barrow Motor Ability Test for College Men (*1*)
2. Iowa-Brace Test of Motor Educability for Grades 4 through 12, Boys and Girls (*12*)
3. Johnson Test of Motor Educability (*5*)
4. Johnson-Metheney Test of Motor Educability for Secondary School Level (*14*)
5. Newton Motor Ability Test for Secondary School Girls (*17*)

TABLE 5.
Latchaw Achievement Scales for Boys and Girls
Vertical Jump
(Inches)

T-Score	Girls Grade IV	Girls Grade V	Girls Grade VI	Boys Grade IV	Boys Grade V	Boys Grade VI	Percentile
76		16			17	19	99
73						18	98
72	14		16	15		17	98
71					16		98
70		15					97
68			15				96
67	13					16	95
66		14		14	15		94
64			14				92
63		13				15	90
62	12						88
60				13	14		84
59		12				14	81
58			13				78
57	11				13		75
56				12		13	72
53		11					61
52			12	11	12		57
51	10					12	53
50							50
48				10			42
47		10	11		11		38
46						11	34
45	9						30
43				9			24
42		9	10	10			21
40	8					10	15
39			9				13
38				8			11
37		8			9		9
35	7					9	6
34			8		8		5
33				7			4
32		7					3
30						8	2
29					7		2
28	6			6			2
27			7				1
24		6		5		7	1

TABLE 6.

Latchaw Achievement Scales for Boys and Girls
Standing Broad Jump
(Feet)

	Girls			Boys			
T-Score	Grade IV	Grade V	Grade VI	Grade IV	Grade V	Grade VI	Percentile
76	5-6			6-2	6-3	6-5	99
75							99
74	5-5	5-8		6-1			99
73	5-4		5-7	6-0	6-2		98
72	5-3			5-11	6-1	6-4	98
71	5-1			5-10			98
70	5-0			5-8	6-0		97
69		5-7		5-7		6-3	97
68		5-6		5-6			96
67					5-11	6-2	95
66	4-11	5-5	5-5	5-5	5-9	6-1	94
65		5-4		5-4	5-8	6-0	93
64		5-2	5-4		5-7	5-11	92
63	4-10	5-1	5-3	5-3	5-6	5-10	90
62	4-9	5-0	5-2	5-2	5-5	5-9	88
61	4-8	4-11	5-1	5-1	5-4	5-8	86
60		4-10			5-3	5-7	84
59	4-7	4-9	5-0	5-0		5-6	81
58		4-8	4-11	4-11	5-2	5-5	78
57	4-6	4-7	4-10		5-1	5-4	75
56	4-5	4-6	4-9	4-10		5-3	72
55	4-4	4-5	4-8	4-9	5-0	5-2	69
54	4-3	4-4		4-8			65
53	4-2	4-3	4-7		4-11	5-1	61
52	4-1		4-6	4-7	4-10	5-0	57
51		4-2	4-5	4-6			53

TABLE 6. (Continued)

	Girls			Boys			
T-Score	Grade IV	Grade V	Grade VI	Grade IV	Grade V	Grade VI	Percentile
50	4-0	4-1	4-4		4-9	4-11	50
49	3-11	4-0		4-5	4-8	4-10	46
48	3-10		4-3		4-7	4-9	42
47		3-11	4-2	4-4	4-6	4-8	38
46	3-9		4-1			4-7	34
45		3-10		4-3	4-5		30
44			4-0	4-2	4-4		27
43	3-8	3-9	3-11		4-3	4-6	24
42				4-1	4-2		21
41		3-8	3-10	4-0	4-1	4-5	18
40	3-7			3-11	4-0		15
39		3-7	3-9	3-10	3-11	4-4	13
38		3-6				4-3	11
37	3-6	3-5	3-8	3-9	3-10	4-2	9
36		3-4	3-7	3-8		4-1	8
35		3-3	3-6	3-5	3-9		6
34	3-5			3-3		4-0	5
33	3-4	3-2					4
32	3-3	3-1	3-5	3-2		3-11	3
31	3-2	3-0	3-4	3-1	3-8	3-10	3
30	3-1	2-11	3-3			3-9	2
29		2-10	3-2			3-7	2
28	3-0	2-9	3-0			3-6	2
27	2-11	2-8	2-11			3-5	1
26	2-10			3-0		3-4	1
25							1
24	2-9		2-10		3-7	3-3	0

TABLE 7.

Latchaw Achievement Scales for Boys and Girls
Shuttle Run
(.1 Seconds)

T-Score	Girls Grade IV	Girls Grade V	Girls Grade VI	Boys Grade IV	Boys Grade V	Boys Grade VI	Percentile
77			11.2				99
76		11.6		11.0	11.2	10.0	99
75						10.2	99
74	12.0		11.3	11.1		10.3	99
73			11.4		11.3	10.4	98
72		11.7		11.3	11.4	10.5	98
71	12.1			11.4		10.6	98
70	12.2	11.8	11.5	11.6		10.7	97
69	12.3	11.9		11.7	11.5	10.8	97
68	12.4			11.8		10.9	96
67		12.0	11.6		11.6	11.0	95
66		12.1	11.7	11.9	11.7		94
65	12.5	12.2	11.8	12.0	11.8	11.1	93
64	12.7	12.3	11.9	12.2	11.9	11.2	92
63	12.9	12.4	12.1	12.3	12.0	11.3	90
62			12.2	12.4		11.4	88
61	13.0		12.3		12.1		86
60	13.1	12.5		12.5	12.2		84
59	13.2	12.6	12.4		12.3	11.5	81
58		12.7		12.6	12.4		78
57	13.3	12.8	12.5	12.7		11.6	75
56	13.4	12.9		12.8		11.7	72
55		13.0	12.6	12.9	12.5	11.8	69
54	13.5	13.1		13.0		11.9	65
53	13.6	13.2	12.7	13.1	12.6		61
52	13.8	13.3	12.8	13.2		12.0	57
51	13.9	13.4	12.9	13.3	12.7		53

TABLE 7. (*Continued*)

| | Girls | | | Boys | | | |
T-Score	Grade IV	Grade V	Grade VI	Grade IV	Grade V	Grade VI	Percentile
50	14.0			13.4	12.8	12.1	50
49	14.1	13.5	13.0		12.9	12.2	46
48	14.2		13.1	13.5	13.0	12.3	42
47	14.3	13.6	13.2		13.1	12.4	38
46	14.4		13.3	13.6	13.2	12.5	34
45	14.5	13.7	13.4	13.7	13.3	12.6	30
44	14.6	13.8		13.8	13.4	12.7	27
43	14.8	13.9	13.5	13.9	13.5	12.9	24
42	14.9		13.6	14.1		13.0	21
41	15.0	14.0	13.7	14.2	13.6	13.1	18
40	15.1		13.8	14.3	13.7	13.2	15
39	15.2	14.1	13.9	14.4		13.4	13
38	15.3	14.2	14.0	14.5	13.8	13.5	11
37	15.4	14.3	14.2		13.9	13.5	9
36	15.5	14.4	14.4	14.6		13.7	8
35	15.6		14.6	14.7	14.0	13.9	6
34	15.8		14.7	14.8	14.1	14.0	5
33	16.0	14.5	14.9	14.9	14.3	14.3	4
32	16.1	14.7	15.0		14.4	14.5	3
31	16.3	14.9	15.1	15.0	14.6	14.6	3
30	16.5	15.1			14.8	14.7	2
29		15.4	15.2		14.9	14.8	2
28	16.6	15.6	15.3		15.0	14.9	2
27	16.7	15.8	15.4		15.1	15.0	1
26	16.8	15.9	15.5			15.1	1
25						15.3	1
24	16.9	16.0		15.1	15.9	15.4	1
23			15.6			15.5	0

TABLE 8.

Latchaw Achievement Scales for Boys and Girls
Softball Repeated Throws

	Girls			Boys			
T-Score	Grade IV	Grade V	Grade VI	Grade IV	Grade V	Grade VI	Percentile
78	9	10					99
76				12			99
74			12			15	99
73				11	14		98
72	8	9					98
68					13	14	96
66			11				94
65				10			93
64					12		92
63	7					13	90
61			10				86
60					11		84
58				9		12	78
55		8	9		10		69
54						11	65
51				8	9		53
49			8			10	46
48		7					42
47	6						38
46					8		34
45			7	7			30
44						9	27
41	5						18
40		6			7		15
39				6		8	13
38			6				11
35	4						6
33				5		7	4
32		5			6		3
29			5				2
28	3	4				6	2
27				4			1
24		3	4		5	5	1

TABLE 9.

Latchaw Achievement Scales for Boys and Girls Basketball Wall Pass

T-Score	Girls Grade IV	Grade V	Grade VI	Boys Grade IV	Grade V	Grade VI	Percentile
77				24	27		99
76	19						99
75			22	23	26	30	99
74					25		99
73		20		22	24		98
72	18				23	29	98
71				21	22	28	98
70						27	97
69						26	97
68	17		21		21	25	96
67		19				24	95
66				20			94
65						23	93
64		18	20				92
63	16	17		19	20		90
62						22	88
61				18			86
60	15		19		19		84
59		16		17			81
58						21	78
57			18		18		75
56	14	15		16			72
55							69
54			17			20	65
53					17		61
52	13	14					57
51			16			19	53

TABLE 9. (Continued)

T-Score	Girls Grade IV	Girls Grade V	Girls Grade VI	Boys Grade IV	Boys Grade V	Boys Grade VI	Percentile
50	12				16		50
49						18	46
48			15	14			42
47	11	13			15		38
46						17	34
45	10		14				30
44		12		13	14		27
43	9						24
42			13			16	21
41		11		12	13		18
40	8						15
39		10			12	15	13
38			12				11
37				11	11		9
36	7	9				14	8
35			11				6
34		8		10	10		5
33			10				4
32	6	7				13	3
31				9	9		3
30			9				2
29					8		2
28		6			7		2
27				8			1
26	5						1
25			8		6	12	1

TABLE 10.

Latchaw Achievement Scales for Boys and Girls
Volleyball Wall Volley

T-Score	Girls			Boys			Percentile
	Grade IV	Grade V	Grade VI	Grade IV	Grade V	Grade VI	
77			21			29	99
76		18					99
75						28	99
74	13	17				27	99
73		15	20	20		26	98
72	12	14			20		98
71	11	13	19	18		25	98
70				16		24	97
69	10		18	15			97
68		12		14	19		96
67			17	13		23	95
66	9			12	18	22	94
65		11		11	17	21	93
64			16		16		92
63	8	10	15		15	20	90
62			14	10		19	88
61		9			14	18	86
60			13				84
59	7		9			17	81
58		8	12		13		78
57			11		12	16	75
56	6	7		8	11		72
55			10				69
54					10	15	65
53	5		9	7			61
52		6			9	14	57
51							53

TABLE 10. (Continued)

T-Score	Girls Grade IV	Grade V	Grade VI	Boys Grade IV	Grade V	Grade VI	Percentile
50	4		8	6	8	13	50
49							46
48		5			7	12	42
47						11	38
46	3		7	5			34
45						10	30
44					6		27
43		4				9	24
42			6	4		8	21
41					5		18
40	2						15
39		3				7	13
38				3			11
37			5		4	6	9
36							8
35						5	6
34		2		2			5
33							4
32	1				3	4	3
31							3
30			3			3	2
29		1					2
28							2
27						2	1
26				1			1
25							1
24					2	1	1
23			2				0

Latchaw Achievement Scales for Boys and Girls
Soccer Wall Volley

| | Girls | | | Boys | | | |
T-Score	Grade IV	Grade V	Grade VI	Grade IV	Grade V	Grade VI	Percentile
76		15		14	16		99
74	13					18	99
73		14			15		98
71				13		17	98
70		13	13				97
69	12					16	97
68					14		96
67						15	95
66	11	12	12				94
65					12		93
64		11			13	14	92
63	10						90
61			11		12		86
60		10		11		13	84
59	9						81
57			10		11		75
56		9		10		12	72
54	8						65
53			9	9	10	11	61
52		8					57
49	7					10	46
48			8	8	9		42
46		7					34
44	6					9	27
43			7	7	8		24
40		6				8	15
39					7		13
38			6	6			11
37	5						9
35						7	6
34		5					5
32			5				3
29	4					6	2
27		4		4			1
26			4				1
24			3	3	5	5	0

Selected References

1. Barrow, Harold, "A Test of Motor Ability for College Men," *Research Quarterly*, Vol. 25, No. 3: 253-260, October, 1954.

2. Brace, David K., *Measuring Motor Ability*. New York: A. S. Barnes & Co., 1927.

3. Bulletin of the California State Department of Education, *Evaluating Pupil Progress*. Sacramento: California State Department of Education, December, 1960.

4. Davies, Evelyn A., *The Elementary School Child and His Posture Patterns*. New York: Appleton-Century-Crofts, Inc., 1955.

5. Johnson, Granville, "Physical Skill Tests for Sectioning Classes into Homogeneous Units," *Research Quarterly*, Vol. 3, No. 1: 128-136, March, 1932.

6. Joint Committtee on Health Problems in Education, American Medical Association-National Education Association, *Health Appraisal of School Children*. Washington 6, D.C.: National Education Association, 1957.

7. Karpovich, Peter V., *Physiology of Muscular Activity*. Philadelphia: W. B. Saunders Company, 1959.

8. Larson, Leonard A., "A Factor Analysis of Motor Ability Variables and Tests, with Tests for College Men," *Research Quarterly*, Vol. 12, No. 3: 499-517, October, 1941.

9. Larson, Leonard A. and Rachael D. Yocom, *Measurement and Evaluation in Physical, Health, and Recreation Education*. St. Louis: The C. V. Mosby Company, 1951.

10. Latchaw, Marjorie, "Measuring Selected Motor Skills in Fourth, Fifth, and Sixth Grades," *Research Quarterly*, Vol. 25, No. 4: 439-449, December, 1954.

11. Lowman, Charles L. and Carl Haven Young, *Postural Fitness*. Philadelphia: Lea & Febiger, 1960.

12. McCloy, C. H., "An Analytical Study of the Stunt Type Tests as a Measure of Motor Educability," *Research Quarterly*, Vol. 8, No. 3: 46-55, October, 1937.

13. Mathews, Donald K., *Measurement in Physical Education*. Philadelphia: W. B. Saunders Company, 1958.

14. Metheney, Eleanor, "Studies of the Johnson Test as a Test of Motor Educability," *Research Quarterly*, Vol. 9, No. 4: 105-115, December, 1938.

15. Morehouse, Laurence E. and A. T. Miller, *Physiology of Exercise.* St. Louis: The C. V. Mosby Co., 1959.

16. Oermann, Karl C., Carl H. Young, and Mitchell J. Gary, *Conditioning Exercises, Games, Tests.* Annapolis: United States Naval Institute, 1960.

17. Powell, Elizabeth and E. C. Howe, "Motor Ability Tests for High School Girls," *Research Quarterly,* Vol. 10, No. 4: 81-88, December, 1939.

18. Pryor, Helen B., *Width-Weight Tables.* Stanford University, California: Stanford University Press, 1940.

19. Riedman, Sarah R., *The Physiology of Work and Play.* New York: The Dryden Press, 1952.

20. Scott, M. Gladys and Esther French, *Measurement and Evaluation in Physical Education.* Dubuque, Iowa: William C. Brown Company, Publishers, 1959.

21. Sheldon, William Herbert, *Atlas of Men.* New York: Harper & Brothers Publishers, 1954.

22. Wessell, Janet A., *Movement Fundamentals.* Englewood Cliffs, N. J.: Prentice-Hall, Inc., 1961.

23. Wetzel, Norman C., "The Simultaneous Screening and Assessment of School Children," *Journal of Health, Physical Education and Recreation,* 13, December, 1942.

24. ———, *The Treatment of Growth Failure in Children.* Cleveland: National Education Association Service, Inc., 1948.

4

ASSESSMENT OF INDIVIDUAL PRACTICES

EVALUATION COMPETENCIES

To *understand:*

1. *how to develop and use the inventory in identifying individual health practices*
2. *how to develop and use the inventory in identifying the individual's practices in human relationships*
3. *how to use the daily schedule in identifying individual practices*
4. *how to use the anecdotal record in identifying individual practices*

EXPERIENCES FOR THE STUDENT

1. *Construct an inventory to measure health practices. Administer the inventory to another person and interpret the results with him.*
2. *Select a published health practice inventory to be administered to the class. Interpret the results.*
3. *Write a daily schedule. Interpret the data in conference with your instructor.*
4. *Observe one individual over a given period of time and under different conditions. Write an anecdote at each observation. Interpret the data.*

Assessment of individual practices identifies what the individual actually *does* in any aspect of his experiences, his "coping" behavior (9). Coping behavior is what an individual does to solve his problems as he sees them. This is different from "expressive" behavior, which describes the life style of the individual, his characteristic way of doing what he does.

A practice inventory is a check list to report evidence of activities or experiences which are actually performed by the individual. The practice inventory is used to help the student identify what he does. It does not identify *why* he is or is not doing a certain thing. Neither does it determine whether he will or will not change his practices. The practice inventory describes what the individual does do as reported by the individual himself or by an observer.

How to Develop and Use the Inventory in Identifying the Individual's Health Practices

The inventory is useful in finding out what the individual is doing to realize his health potential. Such an inventory is called a "health practice inventory." The individual himself should be involved in the assessment and evaluation of his health practices, for then he will recognize the discrepancies between where he is and where he should be. The recognition of need, which may in turn become his goals, is an important factor in making it possible for him to improve his practices.

The teacher also needs to understand where the individual is in order to help him move from where he is to where he should be for best health.

The process of constructing the inventory provides a good learning experience for students since they must first identify the criteria or ideal state of affairs. If, for example, the student investigates to find out what his nutrition should be for best health, he is more apt to understand and accept its importance to him. He develops a list of the things he should do and checks himself against it to determine whether or not and to what extent he does each item.

Practice inventories which have been constructed and published for general use should include criteria which describe the bases for the items. If the user has not participated in developing the criteria, if he does not know what they are or why they were selected, he may have no reason to believe that he should evaluate himself against them. The teacher who uses practice inventories constructed by others should evaluate the items to be sure that the instrument measures those practices he and the student wish to assess. In order to do this he must first seek out the criteria, if they are not stated, and determine whether or not they are acceptable to him and to the student as directions for action.

An inventory developed by teacher and students is already understood by the student. The criteria are known. The student is already becoming aware of discrepancies between what he does and what he should do. He is more interested in setting up a plan of action to improve his practices.

The criteria to be used in constructing a health practice inventory are the materials and conditions necessary for health. To illustrate, some of these materials and conditions are listed; the derived bases for practice are shown with examples of possible check list items.

Materials and Conditions (in part: see Chapter 2.)	Bases for Practice	Examples of Check List Items
Air	Breathing	I study in a well-ventilated room.
Food	Eating	I eat a balanced diet which includes the basic seven.
Elimination	Defecating, urinating	I have regular habits of elimination.
Rest	Sleeping, relaxing	I get at least eight hours sleep every night.
		I can recognize tensions and relax them when needed.
		I feel rested when I get up in the morning.
Taking care of what one is born with	Caring for skin, teeth, eyes, etc.	I go to the dentist at least twice yearly.
		I have regular yearly medical examination.
Affection	Relating	I have a good friend.
Orientation to the environment	Relating to society and its demands	I feel at ease in most groups.

Teacher and students should first determine which materials and conditions they wish to assess (for example, food) and collect information on best practices in the area. These practices may be itemized and statements or questions constructed for each of the items. Each statement should be specific in order that the student may answer it accurately. Responses may be "Yes," "No," or some degree between the two.

An example of a statement which includes more than one point is: "I get at least eight hours sleep every night in a dark, well-ventilated room." This statement includes three points and should be separated into three specific statements:

	No	Seldom	Usually	Yes
I get at least eight hours sleep every night.	____	____	____	____
I sleep in a dark room.	____	____	____	____
My room is well-ventilated.	____	____	____	____

In constructing statements or questions, it is important to have them uniformly positive or uniformly negative to facilitate interpretation of responses. If the "best" answer to each statement is "Yes," it is much simpler to interpret results than if some "best" answers are "Yes" and some are "No."

When the purpose of the inventory is to identify possible problem areas, a comprehensive list of statements is constructed for assessing thoroughly all of the materials and conditions necessary for health. A carefully constructed published inventory may be very useful for this purpose.

Unfortunately, few published inventories provide criteria statements with their materials, and the teacher would need to check the items on the inventory against the criteria for materials and conditions necessary for health to determine if all areas are examined effectively.

After particular problem areas are identified, such as sleep, food, freedom from poisons, students and teacher may study the particular areas and develop their own practice inventory for the selected areas. An illustration of an inventory[1] follows:

[1] Bulletin of the Department of Elementary School Principals, Twenty-Ninth Yearbook, Health in the Elementary School. (Washington 6, D.C.: National Education Association, September, 1950), p. 274. Quoted by permission.

Food Score Card

CREDITS	POSSIBLE DAILY SCORE	M	T	W	T	F	S	S
Milk								
2 glasses 10								
4 glasses 20	20							
Fruits								
1 serving 5								
2 servings 10	10							
Vegetables								
2 vegetables and potato (3 in all) 10	10							
If one vegetable is raw 5	5							
If vegetable is yellow or leafy green								
1 serving 5								
2 servings 10	10							
Extra on fruits and vegetables								
If fruits and vegetables include one serving of tomato, strawberries, melons, or citrus fruits								
	10	10						
Cereal Products								
Whole grain, enriched								
1 serving 10								
2 servings 15	15							
Eggs, Cheese, Meat, Dried Beans, or Peas								
1 serving 10								
2 servings 20	20							
TOTAL CREDITS	100							

DEDUCTIONS	POSSIBLE DAILY SCORE	M	T	W	T	F	S	S
Any meal omitted, deduct 10	10							
Tea, coffee, or soft drink, deduct 5	5							
Any "sweet" between meals (candy, cookie, etc.) 5	5							

TOTAL DEDUCTIONS   20

NET SCORE FOR THE DAY

This particular score card was developed for use by elementary school age boys and girls. Numerical values were assigned to each food according to its importance in the daily food needs of each child, with a possible total score of 100. Daily total scores from 85 up were rated "Good," 75 to 85, "Fair," and below 75, "Poor."

The children could score themselves by recording the score each day for each item. The total credits are added for the day, the deductions are subtracted from the total credits and the net score for the day is computed.

Similar charts could be constructed and used with secondary school students and with adults. An excellent food chart is one put out by the Consumer Service Department of General Foods Corporation, 250 North Street, White Plains, New York. This chart lists nutritive value in per cents of minimum daily requirements for an average adult. An individual may check himself to see if his diet is 100%. The chart is a good educational tool.

Yellen (11) constructed a health practice inventory for use at the elementary school level and Johns and Juhnke (6) published an inventory for assessing health practices of secondary school and college students.

The results of a health practice inventory may be used (a) for counseling purposes, (b) for determining experiences in health courses, (c) for modifying experiences in physical education courses and (d) for setting up specific areas of study in health knowledges and attitudes.

How to Develop and Use the Inventory in Identifying the Individual's Practices in Human Relationships

The values of the society or social organization to which the individual belongs, or wishes to belong, modify his behavior to the extent that he is an acceptable member of this group. His culture places pressures on him by prescribing the behaviors acceptable for membership in the culture. These roles which society expects the individual to learn have been called "developmental tasks" and were discussed previously in Chapter 2.

The definition of a task may be peculiar to a specific cultural segment in the United States. It is interpreted into certain behaviors by each neighborhood, family group, community group and is further modified by the way the individual himself sees it.

The teacher and student must first define and clarify the task being learned. The task should be defined in terms of specific behaviors.

For example, individuals may be working on the task of "relating to changing social groups." They may agree that this means learning to live democratically and effectively with others. They may further define this to mean, in their situation, (a) assuming responsibility for self and others, (b) cooperating with others for the group good, (c) accepting and carrying out leadership responsibilities and (d) recognizing the rights and privileges of others to be different.

They proceed to describe this definition in specific behaviors and put the behaviors in check list form.[2]

My Democratic Skills: Self Evaluation

TASK: Relating to changing social groups
THIS MEANS: Living democratically and effectively with others

	I do this	I need to work on this
Assume responsibility for myself and others by		
1. Entering the dressing room by the back door	___	___
2. Putting my purse and jewelry in my basket	___	___

[2] Courtesy of Barbara Burdg, Los Angeles City Schools, Los Angeles, California.

	I do this	I need to work on this
3. Locking the lock on my basket	_____	_____
4. Having a clean blouse and sox every Monday, clean shorts every other Monday	_____	_____
5. Leaving the dressing room as soon as I am dressed and my things are put away	_____	_____
6. Pushing my basket in so that others will not hurt themselves	_____	_____
7. Taking my turn being a "Lost and Found" girl	_____	_____
8. Returning my own towel and any other towels, which are lying around, to the matron	_____	_____

Cooperate with others for the group good by

1. Settling down to class work without being asked to	_____	_____
2. Volunteering when things need to be done	_____	_____
3. Thinking about the group plans and then working to accomplish them	_____	_____
4. Avoiding taking class time for personal problems which could be solved before or after class	_____	_____
5. Helping rather than criticizing other class members	_____	_____
6. Working with the leader for the good of the group	_____	_____
7. Being willing to sacrifice some of my own wishes for the good of the group	_____	_____
8. Accepting suggestions from others and by trying to improve	_____	_____

	I *do* this	I *need* to work on this

Accept and carry out leadership responsibilities by

1. Volunteering for jobs
   Squad leader   ____   ____
   Team captain   ____   ____
   Towel girl   ____   ____
   Lost and Found girl   ____   ____
   Equipment monitor   ____   ____
   Planning committee   ____   ____
   Evaluation committee   ____   ____

2. Finding out the duties of the job and carrying them out   ____   ____

3. Evaluating my work as a leader and trying to improve   ____   ____

Recognize the rights and privileges of others to be different by

1. Being aware of needs of others and trying to help them   ____   ____

2. Trying to know everyone in class, not just my own gang   ____   ____

3. Being courteous to each person   ____   ____

4. Helping each person to be comfortable by being friendly and pleasant   ____   ____

5. Respecting the rights of others to be different   ____   ____

Before this check list may be used effectively by student and teacher, it is necessary for all concerned to understand what is meant by each item. For example, what is meant by "being courteous?" How is courteous behavior manifested? Does it mean looking at a person and listening attentively as he speaks? Does it mean smiling and saying a few friendly words when you meet him on the street? Does it mean the appropriate use of such phrases as "Excuse me," "Thank you very much," "Please"?

Frequently it is easier to describe the negative behaviors. It is *not* courteous to interrupt others rudely, to make remarks which make others uncomfortable, to belittle or to ridicule others. If such is the case, it may be helpful to construct a check list with positive behaviors in one column and negative behaviors in another column. The student may then check what he does and what he does not do. An illustration of such a check list follows:

My Courtesy Rating

MY NAME   John Jones   MY GRADE   4

	YES	NO		YES	NO
I listen when others are talking and wait until they finish before I talk.			I talk when I want to. If others are talking, I interrupt them.		
I smile and say, "Hello" to everyone in our class.			I don't speak to the people in our class whom I dislike.		
I play with anyone in the class who wants to play.			I play only with my friends. We don't let others play with us.		
I try not to hurt anyone's feelings by doing or saying things which are unkind.			My friends and I make fun of the kids we don't like. We whisper about them and call them names.		

In addition to self-evaluations, teacher evaluation of students and student evaluation of each other are important. If there is a discrepancy between the way the student sees himself and the way others see him, the evaluation data may help him to understand himself better. To illustrate this point, a young man in one of the author's classes had evaluated himself as extremely democratic, helpful to others and well-accepted by his classmates. His group's evaluation of him showed that they thought he was dictatorial, opinionated, selfish, stubborn and a poor group member. After discussing the evaluation results with the instructor, the student decided to find out specifically from his group what he was doing to make them feel this way. He discovered that he felt he was very democratic when he said enthusiastically, "Let's do so and so," and then proceeded to force everyone to do it by refusing to discuss any other possibility. He believed that he was helpful to others when he told them what to do "for their own good." Because the other group members were still trying to be courteous, even though the resentment and antagonism was rapidly reaching the explosive stage, he believed that he was well-liked and well-accepted.

Practice inventories may be constructed to assess recreational practices in the use of leisure time and movement experiences performed in the tasks of daily living.

In summary, the practice inventory is constructed by (a) determining the criteria for best practices, (b) constructing positive statements, each statement concerned with one specific point and (c) setting up categories for the respondent to check which indicate what he does. The inventory is used to assess coping behavior—what the individual does to cope with situations in his life as he sees them.

How to Use the Daily Schedule in Identifying Individual Practices

The daily schedule is an inventory of the daily activities of the individual over a particular period of time. Such an inventory will give the teacher or leader information about the individual in his world. This may include health practices, such as amount of sleep, food intake, activity and it may include social life, friends, recreational pursuits. It may also include the individual's feelings toward the described experiences.

A weekly schedule will of course give more data than a daily schedule. Individuals, however, are less likely to keep an accurate record of their activities for a week as for a day. On the report of the happenings of one day, the individual may indicate where deviations from a "typical" day in his life occur.

Some examples of daily schedules are given to illustrate this data-collecting procedure. The first example is a daily schedule written by a college senior. The students were asked to describe one day from the time they awakened in the morning until they went to bed at night, showing the time a situation or activity occurred and one's feeling about it. They were asked to report specifically the day's food intake and to indicate whether the described activity was performed alone or with others.

Daily Schedule

John _____   Thursday, Sept. 29

TIME	ACTIVITY	FEELING
5:00 A.M.	Alarm clock rings. I get out of bed, shower, brush teeth, then warm Kathy's bottle (Kathy is 6 weeks old —our first baby.)	Tired
5:30	Change Kathy's diaper and give her the bottle.	Tired
6:00	Call wife. Put on coffee while wife showers.	Still tired
6:30	Breakfast with wife. Menu: orange juice, 2 eggs, 2 pieces toast, 3 cups coffee (I am a heavy coffee drinker), 2 cigarettes.	Better
7:00	Wife catches bus for work. I bathe baby.	O.K.
7:30	I get ready to go to class. Try to study a little while baby naps.	Defeated. I can't seem to concentrate.
8:30	Baby sitter arrives. He is a friend, senior law student. I go to class. I walk; we live near campus.	Hurried
9:00	Class	Sleepy. The professor lectures in a mono- tone and I try to keep my eyes open (they say he grades on look- ing alert.)
9:50	Run clear across campus to my next class.	Hurried
10:00	Class	I am really interested in this class (I think) but I'm still tired.
10:50	Class over. Hurry home so baby sit- ter can get to his 12:00 o'clock class. Bottle, burp, and change the baby. Our only salvation is that she is a very good baby.	Hurried. There is never time for any- thing.

Daily Schedule

John _____   Thursday, Sept. 29

TIME	ACTIVITY	FEELING
11:30	Fix my lunch. Menu: sandwich (cold meat and cheese), 3 cups coffee. Study. Leave sandwich makings for baby sitter.	Tired
1:00 P.M.	Baby sitter arrives. I go to class.	Better. This is a lab class and I'm not so sleepy working in it.
1:30	Class. I was late today, but since it is a lab class, no one seemed to notice.	
4:00	Leave for home.	Thankful my classes are over for the day.
4:30	Baby sitter leaves until tomorrow. Play with baby. Relax and wait for wife to get home.	Good
5:30	Wife arrives. We get dinner together. She takes care of baby.	Good
6:30	Dinner with wife. Menu: hamburger, green beans, mashed potatoes, lettuce and tomato salad, bread, cookies, coffee.	Hungry
7:00	Study. Wife does housework and takes care of baby.	Tired. (Wife says that I should write SHE'S tired too.)
10:00	Wife and I have apple and glass of milk. Wife goes to bed. I study.	Tired and bored.
11:00	Bed.	And at 5:00 A.M. it starts all over again.

This is a typical day for Tuesday and Thursday. Monday, Wednesday and Friday I have a class at 11:00 and at 2:00. Saturday I work in a grocery store from 9:00 A.M. to 6:00 P.M.

From this daily schedule the teacher raised questions to be discussed further with the student in a personal interview:

1. Is it necessary for the wife to work to help support the family?

2. The student indicates that he is tired most of the time. His diet seems to be adequate. Could he manage to get more sleep?

3. He appears to have very little (if any) recreation. Could this also contribute to his tired and bored feeling?

4. Is his health good? Has he had a medical examination recently?

5. He is carrying a full load of course work and helps to manage a house and care for a baby. Might it be wiser (even essential) for him to spread his schooling over a longer period by taking a lighter load of courses? Does he need to work on Saturday?

6. Is he bored with his courses because he is tired or is he really not interested in the particular field he has chosen? Should he have vocational counseling?

7. He has indicated one friend who baby-sits. Does he have other friends? Do he and his wife have any social life together?

The second example of a daily schedule is one obtained from a ninth-grade girl. The physical education teacher[3] of the class asked each student to write a daily schedule for this particular day, beginning with when they got up in the morning and continuing until they went to bed. She asked each student to take paper and pencil and write the situations and activities that had happened to them so far today, showing the time of the occurrence, and their feeling about it. She also asked them to show with whom they did the activity and to indicate the food they ate.

To illustrate her explanation she wrote her daily schedule on the chalk board from the time she got up in the morning to the time of the class meeting. The students all started their schedules during the class period and agreed to continue them throughout the day and give them to the teacher on the following day.

Daily Schedule

Mary _____   Monday, October 20

TIME	ACTIVITY	FEELING
6:00	Get up.	Oh—*tired*—not enough sleep this week-end. Oh.
6:10	Shower.	Oh that feels good. I'm awake.
6:30	Made breakfast and ate it.	I stuffed myself with orange juice, cereal, toast, and milk.

[3] Courtesy of Barbara Burdg, Los Angeles City Schools, Los Angeles, California.

Daily Schedule

Mary_____   Monday, October 20

TIME	ACTIVITY	FEELING
7:00	Got dressed.	I felt bad so I didn't care what I wore today.
7:30	Got bus.	I felt a mess because I had to run down the hill to the bus—fast.
7:30 to 8:05	Bus Ride.	Got in a good mood by cracking jokes with John and George.
8:05	Met Jim.	We talked about the week-end with Al, Sally, Jack, Alice, Harry, Eddy, and Bob. Now I really feel neat. I guess it's all Jim's fault.
8:15 to 8:25	Jim walked me to my class.	I opened my locker and couldn't get my books out. Jim to the rescue.
8:25	Homeroom.	I forgot my money for the annual—darn it.
9:00	Gym.	Carol was absent so I took roll with calling the class to order. Boy, I am in a good mood!
9:35	Walked to class.	I beat Kathie out of the gym for once.
9:40	French.	I did good in class today. I got an A on a French Test. I even know the answers today.
10:30	Nutrition.	I'm on a diet so no nutrition today. Talked to Jim *again!!*
11:00	Walked to class.	Jim walked me to gym office.
11:00 to 11:40	Gym office.	Mrs. A. had a lot of work for me to do. I tried. Boy do those B-7 kids have weird answers to questions on the test I corrected.
11:50	Walked to class.	I'm getting tired and sleepy again. To bed early tonight!
11:50 to 12:35	Math.	I almost fell asleep in that class. It was so boring.

Daily Schedule

Mary_____

Monday, October 20

TIME	ACTIVITY	FEELING
12:35 to 1:25	Lunch.	I ate my sandwich in the cafe with Alice, Carol, Mae, Helen and Kathie. After I went out to the lunch area Jim called me over to his post. You see he asked me to go steady Saturday. I said Yes. So at lunch he gave me his St. Christopher. Boy is this ever my lucky day.
1:25	English.	Mr. K. was his funny self today. We learned about verbs.
2:20	Social Studies	Mr. K. was very pleased with our report to the class.
3:10	School's out.	I rode home on the bus and sat with Kathie.
4:00	Homework.	I put on my bathing suit and went down by the pool and studied.
6:00	Dinner.	I set the table and started dinner.
6:15 to 6:40	Stauffer	We have a Stauffer table which reduces you. I studied my French on it.
6:50 to 7:30	Dinner.	We had beef, vegetables, and salad.
7:30 to 9:00	Telephone. Extra Credit.	I spent the rest of the evening on the *phone* and doing extra credit work for school.
9:00 to 9:30	Got ready for bed.	Set hair, washed up, cleaned room, cleaned shoes, and laid out clothes.
9:30	Bed.	Boy, it's been a neat day! Night!

No particular problem areas were indicated in the preceding daily schedule. The individual seems to be happy and positive in her feelings, is successful in her work and in her friendships. In contrast is the following report from another ninth-grade girl.

Daily Schedule

Marjorie _____   Monday, October 20

TIME	ACTIVITY	FEELINGS
6:00	Alarm rings because my sister is on the 7:30 schedule at West High.	I think it is very unfair for the kids and their families.
7:05	I get up.	I feel tired and sick.
7:15	Got dressed.	Couldn't find anything to wear. I'd like to have $1000 to buy a new wardrobe with.
7:30	Brushed my teeth.	I think someone else has been using my toothbrush.
7:32	Took curlers out and combed my hair.	I'd like to cut it off and wear a wig.
7:35	Had a fight with my mother.	I don't like her and she doesn't understand me. I think I'm not really her child.
7:40	Just made the bus. I brought my toast with me and used the mirror to comb my hair. On the bus I talked to Gerald, Anne, John, Carl, Dan, Flip, Sue, and a couple of others I don't know but they know me.	The toast tasted very good because this morning I didn't have breakfast. My hair still looks absolutely horrid. George (the bus driver) says he's going to turn the bus into a Beauty Salon for me. I like everyone on the bus and George is a real blast! He's always telling us about his life.
8:05	Get to school and put gym clothes in locker.	My hair still looks a mess.
8:20	Bell rings and I go to homeroom. Take roll and mark Nan, Scotty, and Danny absent. Danny came in tardy.	I wish people wouldn't be tardy. It's a lot of extra work for me.
8:40	Went to the gym. We didn't play. We wrote down what we had done.	I was really in the mood to play today. (Your tan looks good.)

Daily Schedule

Marjorie _____   Monday, October 20

TIME	ACTIVITY	FEELINGS
9:30	Went to Glee Club. We went down to rehearse with Boys' Glee Club.	I think the boys in the Boys' Glee Club are creeps (they are all 7-A boys).
10:30	Went to nutrition. Forgot my lunch. I went back and got it. Ate or gave away practically all of my lunch. Chicken sandwich, apple, cookies.	I gave away the apple and cookies because I've got to lose weight.
10:45	Went to Algebra. We had a short quiz and worked problems. We reviewed for a test tomorrow.	I practically died of boredom in this class. The teacher doesn't teach well at all. I'll get an "F."
11:40	Went to Social Studies. In the hall my purse opened up and while I was picking the things up, I knocked someone else's books down. When I got into class my books fell all over, and my pencil would *not* sharpen right until it was about an inch long.	Everything is going wrong and I'm in a terrible mood. I told everyone not to talk to me.
12:00	We have television in our room, so we watched the news.	I wish we could watch a movie or quiz show.
12:35	Went to lunch. Since I didn't have any lunch left (I'd given my potato chips away 4th period) I bought some ice cream.	Potato chips make me thirsty but ice cream is fattening.

Daily Schedule

Marjorie _____   Monday, October 20

TIME	ACTIVITY	FEELINGS
1:00	Went to the library.	Wish I were somewhere else.
1:15	Went into Mr. L.'s room to talk to Anne.	Don't think Mr. L. appreciated me sitting on desks.
1:24	Went into French.	My grades are terrible.
2:15	Went to English.	I really have to study those spelling words.
3:10	Get out of school and went to my cousin's house.	The reason I go to my cousin's house so often is because a 15 year old boy lives next door. He is in A-10 at West High.
3:35	Went to the drug store for a coke. Six real darling boys were there.	Think I'll go to my cousin's house more often.
4:00	Got to my cousin's house and my older cousin drove us to Blank's to pick up the ironing.	I wish my cousin would drive more carefully. He is very good, but a show-off.
5:30	Got back to their house and walked home. They were going to eat dinner.	You meet such *interesting* people walking down Beverly Glen. Two boys in a red sports car were honking their horn and passing me very slow but I just ignored them.
6:00	Got home and ate dinner. We had lamb chops, hash brown potatoes, milk, broccoli, fruit cocktail, and cookies.	I liked the dinner very much. I was hungry.
7:00	Tried on a navy blue skirt and my costume for the Mother and Daughter Tea.	The skirt fit well but I don't like navy blue.

Daily Schedule

Marjorie _____   Monday, October 20

TIME	ACTIVITY	FEELINGS
7:30	Read the Sunday paper. I never have a chance to get it on Sunday.	Funny.
8:00	Dried dinner dishes. Had to wash almost every one over because my sister washed them.	My sister sure is a lousy dish washer.
8:30	Started homework. I did this.	Getting tired.
9:15	Moved homework into dining room.	About to fall asleep.
10:00	Had a fight with my mother because she wanted me to go to bed.	She doesn't understand how important homework is.
10:40	Too tired to finish. I covered my bird, set my hair, brushed my teeth, put on my night clothes and went to bed.	I hope I have a better luck with my hair tomorrow.
10:50	Set the alarm to go off at 4:30 so I could finish my homework.	I doubt if I'll be able to get up then but I have to.

P.S. I didn't get up because when I pulled out the alarm I stopped the clock.

The large problem areas indicated in this daily schedule include food, rest, relaxation and sleep, belonging and being valued, success and recognition, orientation to the environment. It would be important to collect further data concerning status, practices and motives before determining the specific areas of need and how to help this individual cope with them.

How to Use the Anecdotal Record in Identifying Individual Practices

The anecdotal record describes an incident or a series of incidents in the life of the individual. The observer records exactly what he sees. Any analysis or interpretation of the recorded incident is written separately from the anecodate with appropriate labelling to identify it from the anecdote.

More than one anecdote is needed to give a picture of an individual's practices. Enough anecdotes must be recorded to show the behaviors of the individual. If an effort is made to draw conclusions from one anecdote, the picture of the individual may be greatly distorted, since one anecdote may not describe the typical behavior of the individual. Typical behavior, however, is likely to recur and several anecdotes are more likely to reveal such behavior (3).

Anecdotes need not be long and complicated. A series of short anecdotes recorded at different times and on different occasions will demand very little of the teacher's time and will provide a systematic set of data which will be of real value to the teacher or leader in helping to understand the individual.

Eight anecdotes are given to illustrate the use of this technique. These anecdotes recorded the behavior of an eleventh-grade girl. Three by five inch cards were used, with each card having the following information recorded on it: (*a*) name of the student; (*b*) date of the observation; (*c*) time of the observation; (*d*) place and circumstances; (*e*) the anecdote.

Anecdotes

2-6, 9:15, SOCIAL DANCE CLASS, GYMNASIUM

Stood at side of gym by herself, watching dancers. When record stopped playing, she came over to me and asked if she could run the record player. I agreed, and she did so.

2-23, 9:00, VOLLEYBALL, FIELD

She came to field by herself. Had not dressed (other girls were in dressing room preparing for class.) I asked her why she wasn't dressed for activity. She said she had forgotten her clothes, had taken them home over the weekend to clean them. She asked if she could be official timer for the volleyball tournament today. I agreed and suggested she talk to the captain of the tournament.

3-3, 9:30, STUNTS AND TUMBLING, GYMNASIUM

Is sitting on floor watching her group perform stunts. Refuses her turn when it comes. Takes record card from floor and says to group leader, "Shall I record the checks for you as they do the stunt?" Can't hear what leader says but she must have agreed. She records checks for the group.

3-4, 9:00, STUNTS AND TUMBLING, GYMNASIUM

Is not dressed for class. Tells me she sprained her back. Says she will record for her group today.

3-18, 9:40, CREATIVE DANCE, GYMNASIUM

Is sitting on floor, beating drum for her group while they dance.

3-20, 9:30, CO-ED BADMINTON, GYMNASIUM

Is playing badminton. Her partner (boy) laughs and says something to her. She laughs and smiles.

3-27, 9:05, CO-ED BADMINTON, GYMNASIUM

She is dressed early and is practicing badminton with another early bird (girl).

3-30, 9:00, SOFTBALL CLASS, FIELD

She is not dressed for activity. Asked me if she could be a towel checker and official scorer during softball unit. I suggested we set up a conference time to discuss what she might do. She smiled and said, "I'd like that." We agreed to set a time at the end of the class period.

These anecdotes show the individual's desire to belong to the group and to be recognized by the group by contributing her services to the group; they also show her real reluctance to participate in the physical education activity, with the exception of co-ed badminton. Could this be due to inadequacy in motor performance or is it chiefly caused by a feeling of not belonging to the group?

Such tools as the movement autobiography, sociometric techniques, measures of strength, endurance, fundamental movement and health and personnel records would provide further information for the teacher in helping the student achieve her potentialities through the class experiences.

To summarize, the practice inventory, daily schedule and anecdotal record are tools with which to identify status—what an individual is actually doing. They do *not* show why he behaves in this particular way. The daily schedule is the most useful technique for helping the teacher or leader obtain a picture of the individual in his environments and his feelings about the world in which he lives. It identifies materials and conditions such as food, sleep, relaxation, feelings and social relationships. It is the one *best* technique for the teacher or leader to use in obtaining an immediate view of the individuals in his group and should be used during the initial contact with the group.

Selected References

1. American Medical Association, *Report of the Second National Conference on Physicians and Schools.* Chicago, 10: American Medical Association, 1949.

2. ———, *Report of the Fifth National Conference on Physicians and Schools.* Chicago, 10: American Medical Association, 1955.

3. Bulletin of the California State Department of Education, *Evaluating Pupil Progress.* Sacramento: California State Department of Education, December, 1960.

4. Bulletin of the Department of Elementary School Principals, Twenty-ninth Yearbook, *Health in the Elementary School.* Washington 6, D.C.: National Education Association, September, 1950.

5. Jacobson, Edmund, *You Must Relax.* New York: Whittlesey House, McGraw-Hill Book Company, Inc., 1948. Third Edition.

6. Johns, Edward B. and Warren L. Juhnke, *Health Practice Inventory.* Stanford, California: Stanford University Press, 1952.

7. Joint Committee on Health Problems in Education, American Medical Association-National Education Association, *Health Appraisal of School Children.* Washington 6, D.C.: National Education Association, 1957.

8. ———, *School Health Services.* Washington 6, D.C.: National Education Association, 1953.

9. Maslow, A. H., *Motivation and Personality.* New York: Harper & Brothers, 1954.

10. Minneapolis Public School Health Service, *Your Child Needs Health.* Minneapolis: Minneapolis Public Schools, Undated.

11. Yellen, Sylvia, *The Development of a Health Practice Inventory for Children in Grades Three, Four, and Five.* Unpublished Master's Thesis, University of California, Los Angeles, June, 1957.

5

ASSESSMENT OF INDIVIDUAL MOTIVES

EVALUATION COMPETENCIES

To *understand*:

1. motivation and its relationship to behavior
2. how to use the informal conversation in identifying individual motives
3. how to use the formal intervew in identifying individual motives
4. how to use unstructured composition in identifying individual motives
5. how to use the interest inventory in identifying individual motives
6. how to use the attitude inventory in identifying individual motives

EXPERIENCES FOR THE STUDENT

1. Read and discuss the meaning of motivation.
2. Construct, administer and interpret interest and attitude inventories.
3. Use role-playing for experience in interviewing, evaluating each interview against the Strang Scale for Rating Interviews:
   a. Select a "case study" which illustrates a typical problem in health education, physical education or recreation;
   b. Role-play an intervew between the individual with the problem and the teacher or leader;
   c. Role-play an interview between the teacher or leader and the child's parents;
   d. Divide into groups and have each group select an interview to role-play, with some groups using poor intervew techniques and other groups using good intervew techniques.
4. Collect data on one individual. In interpreting the data try to understand his motivations.
5. Invite a psychologist or other resource person to help the class members understand the use of projective techniques.

Motives are the forces which direct individual behavior. What causes a person to act in a certain way? Why does he do what he does? The evaluation process is concerned with identifying and clarifying the individual's motives.

Motivation and Its Relationship to Behavior

Historically, educators have believed that the individual was motivated by: (a) basic drives or instincts such as hunger, sleep, temperature regulation; (b) such growth and development characteristics as increase in body size and proportions, motor development, social development; and (c) developmental tasks such as acquiring appropriate independence-dependence relationship.

Motivation theory in the past has frequently considered purpose to be directed by what Maslow (11) calls *deficiency motivation*. That is, the individual's goals are met by determining what he needs in relation to the so-called basic needs, drives or tasks and by providing for the dearth or deficiency. When a person is hungry, he has a deficiency. He eats food and the deficiency is met. He feels drowsy; he sleeps and the deficiency is met. He feels the need for temperature regulation; he turns the control on his electric blanket and the need is met. These deficiencies are gone for a time and may then arise again.

In the same list of drives such as hunger, sleep and temperature regulation are others which are not satisfied and not forgotten when they are met. An example of one of these is the need for affection. When a person receives or gives love, he does not stop needing or wanting affection but may grow in his ability to give and receive love even more generously. Instead of affection satisfying a deficiency which may be alleviated for a time, he continues to grow in his affectional relationships. Maslow (11) calls this *growth motivation*.

If we believe that behavior is directed by basic needs, drives, tasks, we may wonder why one person who needs sleep will meet his need by sleeping and another person who needs sleep will refuse to sleep, even though the conditions for sleeping are available to him; why a person who is hungry will refuse to eat, or a person who is cold will refuse to put on warm clothing even when those conditions are available.

His motives are governed by his perception of what will maintain, enhance and actualize his self (1, 6, 8, 11). If we can understand how the individual perceives himself, we may better understand the goals he is attempting to achieve. When teachers and leaders recognize that the basic need of the individual is to maintain, enhance and actualize his self, their concern is to find out what he pictures to be his "self." In order to provide experiences which will be accepted by the individual, *we must know him.* He selects and works on goals, the attainment of which he believes will enhance and maintain self.

The individual is directed by his goals or purposes, by his aspirations. The person may be aware of his purposes and aspirations or he may be unclear about them and, therefore, unable to express them. He may have his purposes and aspirations well defined or he may need help in clarifying and understanding them. He does what will achieve his purposes as he sees them.

The purposes and aspirations of the individual may be identified by (a) expressions from the individual himself and (b) the use of specially constructed instruments.

Expression of purposes and aspirations in the individual's own words may be obtained through (a) informal conversation, (b) the formal interview and (c) unstructured composition. Instruments which may be constructed and used by the teacher or leader for assessing individual goals and aspirations are (a) interest inventories and (b) attitude inventories.

Other tools for assessing motives are projective techniques, including the Rorschach test, the Thematic Apperception Test (TAT), the word association and sentence completion methods, the Rosenzweig Picture-Frustration method and finger painting (2). These instruments may be used only by psychologists and other individuals who are trained in the administration and interpretation of the tests. Such information may be available in the counseling and guidance office, but it is not usually accessible to the teacher and will not be discussed further in this book.

How to Use the Informal Conversation in Identifying Individual Motives

The teacher or leader should avail himself of any opportunity to talk informally with a student. This does not mean that the teacher is attempting to pry into the student's personal affairs, but it does mean that he is using such a procedure in an effort to know the student better. If proper rapport has been established between teacher and student, they will relate to each other in such a way that the student will want to have the teacher *know* him.

Any other information the teacher or leader may have about the student will add to the effectiveness of the informal conversation. The teacher may explore areas in which he needs further clarification. In turn, informal conversation helps the student know the teacher better. The student is more likely to describe his real concerns and wishes to someone whom he knows and trusts.

Informal conversation either may be carried on with the individual alone or it may include group members if assessment of his group relationships is needed. Such conversations may reveal the purposes and aspirations of the individual although he may not actually state them as such. The teacher or leader may help the person clarify his purposes and aspirations through further discussion. When purposes and aspirations are known, the teacher may help the individual evaluate them and may help him in goal achievement.

Opportunities for informal conversation may occur before the beginning of the class period, at the end of the period and on other chance occasions. An example of an informal conversation in a junior high school physical education class follows. Student and teacher were talking while waiting for the other students to appear from the locker rooms at the beginning of the period.

Teacher: How are things going, Bill?

Student: O.K. I guess. Sure wish we could do something besides these old stunts, though. They're kid stuff!

Teacher: Which activities do you like best, Bill?

Student: The ones we don't do. I think most of this stuff is a waste of time. Why can't we learn golf or something? Or skiing?

Teacher: Do you go skiing?

Student: No, but my Dad is having me take golf lessons from the pro at the club. Anyway, I hate all of this dumb stuff. I'm not always playing games like a lot of these guys. I'm concentrating on being a physicist and I don't think I'll have any use for most of this stuff.

In interpreting this informal conversation the teacher needed other kinds of information. During the class period he noticed that this student had very poor movement skills. He spent most of the stunt period avoiding his turn to perform, making comments under his breath and showing a disdainful attitude toward other members of the group. He appeared to be uncomfortable and actually fearful when he had to perform a stunt.

Certainly, the present selection of movement experience was not helping this student improve his movement skills or enhance his picture of himself in movement. Further information needed by the teacher may include: (a) what kinds of movement experiences has he had previously? (b) are there any movement areas in which he has been successful? (c) what are his recreational interests and pursuits? (d) who are his friends? (e) what does his health record show? (f) what is his family's attitude toward him, his movement skills and toward physical education in general?

Further conversation with the student may provide some answers to these questions if the teacher-student rapport is such that the student will talk freely to the teacher.

How to Use the Formal Interview in Identifying Individual Motives

The formal interview is similar to the informal conversation in that it utilizes discussion between the teacher or leader and student. Unlike the informal conversation, however, it is arranged for a particular purpose and at a given time. The interview may be requested by either the student or teacher, depending upon the purpose.

If the teacher wishes to collect further data to supplement information obtained through written materials, such as the autobiography or daily schedule, through informal conversation or observation, he may request the interview.

Some students may find it difficult to communicate through writing and are better able to do so by talking directly to the teacher. For example, a student may have turned in a very meager autobiography and daily schedule simply because he writes poorly and finds it too time-consuming. The teacher may wish more information about such a student's recreational activities or movement experiences than he was able to describe in writing, and a short interview with the student may be helpful in obtaining such information.

There is always the possibility, however, that the student did not wish to tell more about himself. If such were the case, the teacher's request for further information could be threatening to him. The teacher should avoid probing and should be sensitive to the student's feelings. The interview initiated by the teacher for obtaining certain data may result in the teacher recognizing some of the student's problems relating to the situation and outside help from trained personnel may be indicated.

The teacher or leader has a guidance role to perform but it is important that he does not exceed the limits of his professional training. He is not qualified to take the role of an analyst or consulting psychologist. The teacher or leader with a guidance point of view, however, may be most helpful in providing educational counseling and in referring the student when it is needed. Because of his regular contacts with the student, he is frequently in a position to identify problem areas and provide assistance within his capacity to do so. This is his responsibility and he should prepare himself to work effectively in such a role (5, 9).

The formal interview provides an opportunity for student and teacher to talk together on a one-to-one basis without interruption and outside distractions. The student may feel that he has all of the teacher's attention and that he does not have to share this attention with the other members of his class for this appointed time. This may be helpful in establishing rapport between the teacher and student if the interview is conducted by the teacher for this purpose.

The interview, to give the greatest possible value to the participants, should be held in a private, comfortable setting, free from interruption. Each one of us has undoubtedly had the frustrating experience of attempting to communicate an idea only to be interrupted in the middle of a sentence by the ringing telephone or the casual kibitzer.

Adequate time should be planned for the interview so there is a relaxed feeling rather than a tense, hurried feeling. The time for terminating the interview should also be set and should be adhered to. If there is need for further discussion another appointment may be made, but an interview which continues on and on until both participants are vainly struggling for a graceful way to terminate it may indeed have diminishing returns.

The purpose of the interview should be clear. This should be carefully followed, particularly if the teacher or leader initiates the interview. The student may be apprehensive, and with good reason, when the teacher asks him to set up an appointment "because we have something to discuss." Many students' previous experiences in discussing "something" with the teacher have not had salubrious results in enhancing student "self." Too many times he has been reprimanded in just such a manner and his guilts, fears and defenses immediately begin functioning. The teacher should state specifically why he is requesting the interview, and if the student feels that he either does not have the information requested or does not choose to participate, he should have the privilege of declining without feeling threatened. If factual information is desired, the teacher should have a recording system prepared ahead of time, such as note-taking techniques in check list (or other) form.

When the interview is used exclusively as a counseling technique, it is preferable that it be initiated by the student, directed by the student and decisions should be the responsibility of the student.

Strang[1] has developed an excellent scale for rating interviews against which the teacher or leader may evaluate his interviews.

Strang Scale for Rating Interviews

1. What was the setting for the interview?

Plenty of time scheduled	Insufficient time
Feeling of leisure	People waiting
Privacy	People bustling in and out
Pleasant surroundings, lighting, and other provisions for the interviewee's comfort	Telephone to be answered
	Glare and discomfort

2. What was the appearance and manner of the interviewer?

Pleasant voice	Unpleasant voice
Poise and reasonable self-confidence	Fatigued, dull
At ease	Uncertain and insecure
Cordial	Patronizing
Genuine interest in interviewee	Indifferent

3. How did the interviewee respond conversationally during the interview?

Talked freely	Tended to make "snap" decisions
Tried to think through problem aloud	Refused to talk
	Unwilling to accept his responsibility in the interview

4. How did the interviewer encourage the interviewee to get an understanding of himself and his problem?

[1] Ruth Strang, *The Role of the Teacher in Personnel Work,* 4th ed. (New York: Bureau of Publications, Teachers College, Columbia University, 1953), pp. 389-90. By permission of Ruth Strang.

By repeating his most significant remarks	By being completely passive
By following, in a natural way, clues he interviewee gave	By telling interviewee what to do
By asking questions to clarify certain points	By arguing or criticizing
By summarizing interviewee's remarks and helping him interpret	By probing By monopolizing the discussion

5. How did the attitude of the interviewee change during the interview?

Interviewee gained new and valuable insights and orientation; felt more hopeful and more confident in his ability to handle the situation; became increasingly independent of the interviewer; had a more friendly relationship	Interviewee became increasingly dependent upon the interviewer; little responsibility for thinking through the situation himself; less confident; more hopeless; more resistant to the counselor

6. What kind of plan resulted from the interview?

A plan worked out primarily by the interviewee; realistic and possible of being carried out	A ready-made plan, which the interviewer imposed upon the student

7. What was the effect of the interview on subsequent relationship with the interviewer?

Student was able to carry out plans; came voluntarily to the interviewer when he needed further help	No favorable change in behavior; student avoided coming to the interviewer again

The teacher's role in the counseling process is educational in nature. It is primarily for the purpose of improving the teaching-learning situation by helping the individual examine himself in order that his purposes and aspirations may be more clearly defined. The counseling procedure, like other teaching procedures, may benefit all students; it is not only for the "problem" child. When therapy is needed, the teacher's responsibility is to refer the student to the specialist.

Types of problems where referral is mandatory are: (a) problems relating to health conditions requiring medical attention; (b) problems related to such persistent emotional disturbances, as excessive daydreaming, extreme irritability, change from usual behavior patterns, inability to communicate (c) problems relating to home situations and family difficulties; (d) problems relating to vocational guidance.

How to Use the Unstructured Composition in Identifying Individual Motives

This technique has been used successfully in the guidance and counseling field to help the individual objectify his perceptions about himself. Some of the procedures for collecting such data are: (*a*) student writes what he likes or does not like about himself; (*b*) student writes what he would like to be; (*c*) student writes how he sees himself as a person and how he thinks others see him.

The health education teacher may use these data to provide some information about the individual's feelings toward himself and others, his individual health problems as he sees them. The physical education teacher may wish to collect information about the student's feelings toward himself in movement situations. The recreation leader may wish further insight into the individual's recreational attitudes, his feelings and desires in regard to the use of leisure time.

A composition written by a ninth grade girl upon the request of her physical education teacher is given as an illustration. The teacher asked the students to write on these three points; (*a*) how I think I move; (*b*) what I think others feel about how how I move; (*c*) how I would like to move.

About Myself in Movement
by

Susan _____

How I think I move.

I feel that I move real good. When I walk or run I feel like I look good. When I am playing games I usually do very well because it is easy for me. I am a good dancer and when I am dancing I feel happy. I learn new movement things easily and enjoy doing all kinds of physical education activities. I would rather be moving than just be watching others move.

What I think others feel about how I move.

Other kids tell me they think I am very good in sports and athletic activities. Both boys and girls say I am a very good dancer. I think others think I move well. I always get an "A" in physical education so my teachers must think I move well too.

How I would like to move.

I like the way I move because I think I do it well. I am not interested in being an Olympic star so I think I am happy with myself as I am. I would like to dive better than I do and I am trying to improve my skiing, but I am really pretty well satisfied with my movement.

In analyzing this student's perceptions of herself in movement, one may wish to consider the following points: (a) what are the student's feelings about movement experiences? (b) is the student realistic about her own movement or do other data indicate that her view is distorted? (c) does the student appear to accept her own movement characteristics? (d) what are her motives, purposes, goals in movement areas? (e) what are the next steps in working with this student and her movement goals?

How to Use the Interest Inventory in Identifying Individual Motives

Interests are a reflection of the individual's perception of what will maintain, enhance and actualize his self; he is interested in the experiences which he believes will do so.

Interests may be confused with attitudes since both are frequently expressed by feelings. Bernard's[2] distinction between the two is the point of view accepted here: "An attitude is a predisposition to act or think in a certain way, while interests are likely to be characterized by active participation." He further states that successful experience stimulates interest. If such is the case, the teacher or leader has a grave responsibility in providing experiences under conditions which will encourage successful performance (3).

The one best criterion for selection of experiences is interest. Lack of interest is a real deterrent to learning and individuals tend to avoid experiences in which they have little interest.

Interest inventories are check lists or questionnaires designed to show individual preference. They are useful in helping the teacher or leader know more about the individuals with whom he is working. Interests and motives are interdependent. By determining individual interests, experiences may be provided which closely relate to individual motives.

Other procedures for determining interests include observing individual practices (does he actually do what he *says* he is interested in doing?) or by providing opportunities for students to indicate their likes and dislikes when evaluating their experiences.

[2] Harold W. Bernard, *Adolescent Development in American Culture* (Yonkers-on-Hudson, New York: World Book Company, 1957), p. 343.

The interest inventory may be constructed to cover a wide range of activities and experiences or it may be specifically directed toward one area. For example, if used to explore recreational interests of individuals, it may include all possible leisure time experiences available in the given community, playground, park or school. Such an inventory may also be useful in opening new avenues of exploration to the individual by presenting experiences in which he has not previously engaged or of which he has not been aware. An illustration of such an inventory follows.

My Leisure Time Interests

My feelings about the experience

ACTIVITY	LIKE THIS VERY MUCH	IT IS O.K.	DON'T KNOW THIS	WOULD LIKE TO LEARN	PREFER NOT TO DO THIS
Bowling	——	——	——	——	——
Painting	——	——	——	——	——
Swimming	——	——	——	——	——
Wood Carving	——	——	——	——	——

If the inventory is to be used as a basis for determining the experiences in a particular unit of work, it may cover only specifics related to the particular material. For example:

Questions I Would Like to Have Answered During Our Health Education Class

	VERY IMPORTANT	IMPORTANT	O.K.	NOT IMPORTANT
ABOUT MY PERSONALITY				
1. How can I tell whether my personality is good or not?	——	——	——	——
2. Is personality inherited?	——	——	——	——
3. How do I know whether I am really grown up?	——	——	——	——
4. _____	——	——	——	——
5. _____	——	——	——	——
ABOUT MY SOCIAL RELATIONSHIPS				
6. What traits are basic to getting along with others?	——	——	——	——

7. What social skills should I know in starting to date? ___ ___ ___ ___
8. How can I learn to be liked? ___ ___ ___ ___
9. Should I go steady? ___ ___ ___ ___
10. _____ ___ ___ ___ ___
11. _____ ___ ___ ___ ___

ABOUT MY FAMILY

12. How can I help my family to recognize that I'm grown up? ___ ___ ___ ___
13. How much allowance should a person my age have? ___ ___ ___ ___
14. Where can I go to get help on my personal problems? ___ ___ ___ ___
15. What should you do about parents? ___ ___ ___ ___
16. _____ ___ ___ ___ ___
17. _____ ___ ___ ___ ___

ABOUT MY BODY

18. What does my body look like under the skin? ___ ___ ___ ___
19. How can I get to be tall? ___ ___ ___ ___
20. What changes take place in a person's body at adolescence? ___ ___ ___ ___
21. What causes acne? ___ ___ ___ ___
22. Is smoking really harmful? ___ ___ ___ ___
23. Is it all right to drink alcoholic beverages? ___ ___ ___ ___
24. What should I do if I find someone taking drugs? ___ ___ ___ ___
25. _____ ___ ___ ___ ___
26. _____ ___ ___ ___ ___

The interest inventory may be used by the physical education teacher to identify movement patterns and to find out individual preferences for activities. Space should be left at the end of an inventory for the students to write in any additional activities they would like to learn.

An illustration of an interest inventory for assessing interests in physical education activities at the high school level follows.

Survey of Interests in
Physical Education

Name_____   Grade_____   Age_____

Check each activity in the column or columns which show your feelings about it. This information will help us in selecting the activities for our physical education classes this semester.

ACTIVITY	I LIKE THIS	I DO NOT LIKE THIS	I HAVE NOT DONE THIS	I WOULD LIKE TO LEARN THIS
Dance:				
Modern Dance	_____	_____	_____	_____
Social Dance	_____	_____	_____	_____
Other	_____	_____	_____	_____
Individual-Dual:				
Badminton	_____	_____	_____	_____
Bowling	_____	_____	_____	_____
Golf	_____	_____	_____	_____
Stunts	_____	_____	_____	_____
Swimming	_____	_____	_____	_____
Tennis	_____	_____	_____	_____
Trampoline	_____	_____	_____	_____
Other	_____	_____	_____	_____
Team Games:				
Soccer	_____	_____	_____	_____
Speedball	_____	_____	_____	_____
Volleyball	_____	_____	_____	_____
Other	_____	_____	_____	_____

Activities included in this particular inventory were selected on the basis of availability in the school situation in relation to equipment, scheduling possibilities, qualified instructors for the various activities, time and space. Many of the classes in this particular high school were coeducational and it was possible to meet student interests and choices in most cases.

How to Use the Attitude Inventory in
· Identifying Individual Motives

An attitude has been defined as "a predisposition to act or think in a certain way." [3] It may also be thought of as "an emotionalized tendency to act for or against something." [4] The individual perceives a situation in a certain way and places some judgment on what he perceives. This judgment is his attitude. It is his "personal meaning of an event." [5]

How an attitude is measured depends upon what is to be measured. One may wish to investigate the individual's feeling about the nature of another individual or of a group of individuals; his belief about the importance of an object or the nature of an object; his tendency to behave in certain ways in certain situations; his beliefs about rules and regulations with respect to a situation; his estimate of the value of another individual, group or object. (13).

Attitudes are appraised through the use of practice inventories, sociometric tools, observation procedures and projective techniques. In addition to these procedures attitude tests may be constructed and used by the teacher or leader.

The teacher or leader has a responsibility for understanding how the individual with whom he works feels about himself, other individuals and objects. His attitude or feeling about something is his directing force. To know his attitude is to understand his motive and this attitude is of prime importance to a teacher or leader who is working with him.

If experiences are organized in a school or recreation program on the basis of what a person feels is important to him individually, he will be able to select meaningful activities from such experiences. An important task of the teacher or leader is to help the individual extend his perceptions. This may be done through the experiences he selects. The teacher or leader, therefore, needs to understand what the individual perceives in order to help him continue his development outward.

The school or recreation program, however, which consists of required experiences which are the same for everyone poses an entirely different problem for the teacher or leader. In such a situation the

[3] Harold W. Bernard, *Adolescent Development in American Culture* (Yonkers-on-Hudson, New York: World Book Company, 1957), p. 343.
[4] Paul L. Dressel, Ed., *Evaluation in the Basic College* (New York: Harper & Brothers, 1958), p. 216.
[5] Arthur W. Combs and Donald Snygg, *Individual Behavior*, Rev. Ed. (New York: Harper & Brothers, 1959), p. 232.

teacher or leader must be able to set up meaningful experiences for each individual within the limits of the required area. Under such circumstances attitude tests are particularly helpful for understanding individual motives.

Simple attitude testing may be done by teachers and leaders. It is essential, however, that trained personnel be used when deeper meanings are needed. Health education leaders, even those who have received particular preparation in such matters, require the assistance of phychologists and medical doctors when assessment extends beyond simple inventories and check lists. Such assistance is needed also in the interpretation of some of the data. Health education, physical education and recreation personnel should learn how to use such trained resource help when it is indicated.

Concern has been expressed by some writers in regard to the role of the teacher or leader in collecting such data in that it may have the connotation of delving into "psychological matters." Parents, not understanding the use of such information or disagreeing with the value of such an approach, may believe that teachers are interfering with home affairs.

Yet, the teacher or leader needs to understand all facets of the individual in order to work with him effectively. If the school is organized so that trained personnel identifies the practices and attitudes of the individual and places him into experiences which are really appropriate for him, the teacher's role is that of determining the individual concerns within the subject matter area. If the school, however, uses no such bases for determining individual programs, many students may be placed within experiences which have little or no value in meeting their particular goals. Under such conditions the teacher or leader would need to use tools for determining individual motives and purposes and serve in a guidance capacity in directing the student experiences. An attitude test is an appropriate instrument for providing information for such purposes. Should the teacher determine that the individual is in the wrong experience for helping him meet his goals, the teacher will work with the individual and others in authority to find the appropriate experience. If it is impossible to do this, the teacher will adjust the present experience to more closely fit the individual's concerns.

The recreation leader may make good use of attitude assessment as a basis for providing leisure time experiences to meet individual purposes.

Constructing an attitude test. The validity of the attitude test is a problem in the construction of the instrument. That is, does the test measure what it professes to measure—the attitude of the individual? Teacher-constructed tests may have limitations in regard to validity and may be a rough measure of attitude. They are useful, however, in better understanding the individual if the data are interpreted in light of other information about the individual. As in using any measuring instrument, interpretation should be done cautiously and with the knowledge that results obtained from any *one* instrument may be misleading.

Because we are concerned with the whole individual in health education, physical education and recreation, many attitude inventories would be based on the materials and conditions necessary for the healthy growth and development of the individual. For example, the teacher or leader may be concerned about the student's attitude toward rest, activity, food or other materials and conditions for growth or he may wish to assess individual attitude toward a particular developmental task such as developing independence from adults through accepting responsibility for one's self.

The *first step,* then, in constructing an attitude inventory is to select the area of concern. To illustrate, let us assume that the teacher is interested in assessing attitudes toward food. A recent survey may have shown that the majority of students in this particular group were not eating breakfast. The specific area of concern may be, in this instance, "eating breakfast."

Second, items are constructed which indicate a range of opinions, both positive and negative, toward eating breakfast. These items should be constructed in such a way that they express only opinions or feelings rather than facts or principles. Corey[6] suggests that one way to obtain a range of opinions toward the particular subject is to have each student write three or four statements which express various viewpoints about the particular subject. From these statements a number are selected which represent a range of opinion, both positive and negative.

The *third* step is to administer this preliminary inventory to the entire group of students. This may be done orally by reading the statement to the students and asking them to indicate whether they consider the statement to be favorable or unfavorable, true or false, agree or disagree, like or dislike, approve or disapprove, depending upon what is to be measured by the inventory. Some statements may need to be

[6] Stephen M. Corey, "Measuring Attitudes in the Classroom," *Elementary School Journal,* XLIII (April, 1943), 457-61.

discarded or re-worded because of ambiguities or unrelatedness to the area of concern. Other statements may be discarded because students do not agree as to their positive or negative nature. It has been suggested that a statement may be used when approximately 80 per cent of the group agree that it is favorable or unfavorable, as the case may be (4).

After a careful analysis of the items and revision where needed, the test is ready for use. Directions to the students should describe the procedure for responding to the items. Usually, agreement is indicated by placing a plus sign before the statement, and disagreement is signified by a minus sign. If the student is uncertain as to whether he agrees or disagrees, he places a zero (0) before the item; another symbol which may be used for this purpose is the question mark.

Another procedure which may be used is to provide categories to be checked by the student. For example:

	STRONGLY AGREE	AGREE	UNDECIDED	DISAGREE	STRONGLY DISAGREE
It is all right to cheat if everyone else is doing it.	_____	_____	_____	_____	_____

Scoring values may be assigned as follows:[7] (a) for favorable statements; strongly agree = 5 points, agree = 4 points, undecided = 3 points, disagree = 2 points, and strongly disagree = 1 point; (b) for unfavorable statements; strongly agree = 1 point, agree = 2 points, undecided = 3 points, disagree = 4 points, and strongly disagree = 5 points. A total score is computed by adding the value obtained for each statement with large totals indicating favorable attitude and smaller total scores showing less favorable attitude.

A similar system may be used where plus scores indicate a favorable attitude and minus scores an unfavorable attitude: (a) for favorable statements; strongly agree = +2, agree = +1, undecided = 0, disagree = −1, strongly disagree = −2; (b) for unfavorable statements; strongly agree = −2, agree = −1, undecided = 0, disagree = +1, and strongly disagree = +2.

Wear (16, 17) developed a scale for measuring attitude toward

[7] Stephen M. Corey, "Measuring Attitudes in the Classroom," Elementary School Journal, XLIII (April, 1943), p. 460.

physical education as an activity course, which may be useful to teachers of physical education at the secondary and college levels. Additional sources which provide further help in the measurement of attitudes are listed in the Selected References. (7, 10, 12, 15)

Selected References

1. Allport, Gordon W., *Becoming*. New Haven: Yale University Press, 1955.

2. Anderson, Harold H. and Gladys L. Anderson, *An Introduction to Projective Techniques*. Englewood Cliffs, N.J.: Prentice-Hall, Inc., 1951.

3. Bernard, Harold W., *Adolescent Development in American Culture*. Yonkers-on-Hudson, New York: World Book Company, 1957.

4. Bulletin of the California State Department of Education, *Evaluating Pupil Progress*, Vol. XXIX, No. 14. Sacramento: California State Department of Education, December, 1960.

5. Cassidy, Rosalind, *Counseling in the Physical Education Program*. New York: Appleton-Century-Crofts, Inc., 1959.

6. Combs, Arthur W. and Donald Snygg, *Individual Behavior*, Rev. Ed. New York: Harper & Brothers, 1959.

7. Edwards, Allen L., *Techniques of Attitude Scale Construction*. New York: Appleton-Century-Crofts, Inc., 1956.

8. Goldstein, Kurt, *The Organism*. New York: American Book Company, 1939.

9. Gordon, Ira J., *The Teacher As a Guidance Worker*. New York: Harper & Brothers, 1956.

10. Likert, Rensis, "A Technique for the Measurement of Attitudes," *Archives of Psychology*, XXII, 1932, pp. 1-55.

11. Maslow, A. H., *Motivation and Personality*. New York: Harper & Brothers, 1954.

12. McNemar, Quinn, "Opinion-Attitude Methodology," *Psychological Bulletin*, XLIII, July, 1946, pp. 289-374.

13. Sellitz, Clarie, Marie Jahoda, Morton Deutsch and Stuart W. Cook, Research Methods in Social Relations. New York: Holt, Rinehart and Winston, Inc., Rev. Ed., 1959.

14. Strang, Ruth, *The Role of the Teacher in Personnel Work*, 4th ed.

New York: Bureau of Publications, Teachers College, Columbia University, 1953.

15. Wang, Charles K. A., "Suggested Criteria for Writing Attitude Statements," *Journal of Social Psychology*, III, August, 1932, pp. 367-76.

16. Wear, Carlos L., "The Evaluating of Attitude Toward Physical Education As An Activity Course," *Research Quarterly*, Vol. 22, No. 1, March, 1951, pp. 114-26.

17. ———, "Construction of Equivalent Forms of An Attitude Scale," *Research Quarterly*, Vol. 26, No. 1, March, 1955, pp. 113-19.

PART THREE

Finding out about THE ENVIRONMENTS

Competencies Needed by Teachers and Leaders in Health Education, Physical Education and Recreation

1. To understand the appraisal of the physical plant

2. To understand the appraisal of climate

3. To understand marking and grading

Objective	Value or Criterion	Measuring Tool
To appraise the physical plant	Predetermined standards contributing to healthy growth and development obtained through scientific investigation	Questionnaire Interview Check list Rating Scale
To appraise the climate	Democratic philosophy in contemporary United States	Check list Rating Scale
To understand marking and grading	Democratic philosophy in contemporary United States	None

6

APPRAISAL OF THE PHYSICAL PLANT

EVALUATION COMPETENCIES

To understand:
1. *foundation facts for evaluating environments*
2. *how to evaluate the physical plant*

EXPERIENCES FOR THE STUDENT

1. *Appraise the physical plant of your particular school or recreation area by:*
    a. *selecting a published check list or rating scale and checking the items you can observe;*
    b. *constructing a questionnaire to elicit information you could not obtain through observation.*
2. *Analyze the data and make recommendations for implementing the results.*

Since the individual and the environment interact as a unit, the environments over which the teacher or leader has some control should be those which contribute most to the healthy growth and development of the individual.

The environment includes everything outside of the skin of the human organism. The teacher or leader is concerned about all of the environments within his jurisdiction and over which he may exert some influence. The child and youth, and adult to a lesser extent, spend a considerable amount of time in schools and other public agencies. The environments provided for them should be instructive rather than destructive.

Foundation Facts for Evaluating Environments

Foundation facts which may help the teacher or leader understand the importance of his role in the environments of the individuals with whom he works include the following:

1. The interaction of the individual within his world influences his

individuality. He becomes what the interaction between the environment and his genes allow (7, 8).

2. The healthy individual is oriented two ways: (*a*) toward his own self determination or self government and (*b*) toward finding a place for himself in the larger world (*1, 7*).

3. The child values himself as he sees how he is evaluated by those whom he values (3, 5, 12, 14).

The environmental factors to be considered by the teacher or leader, therefore, are: (*a*) the physical plant, including school buildings, playgrounds, recreational areas; (*b*) the teacher or leader and the climate he creates; (*c*) the grading and marking which reflects the valuing of the individual.

How to Evaluate the Physical Plant

The evaluation of the physical plant usually includes an appraisal of the school site, the community, school transportation, school plant administration and planning, and financing.

The criteria for the provision and operation of a healthful, safe and sanitary school plant have been developed by specialists in these areas and are available in published form (2, 6, 9, 10, 11, 13, 16). Items included for assessment in many of these instruments are as follows:

1. Site size and utilization

2. Building structure, equipment and grounds

3. Outdoor play areas

4. Lighting

5. Heating and ventilation

6. Noise control

7. Water

8. Handwashing and toilet facilities

9. Fire prevention and drill

10. Civil defense preparedness

11. Health service facilities and personnel

12. Lunchroom and kitchen facilities

13. Gymnasia, athletic play areas and shower rooms

14. Swimming pools

15. Science laboratories and school shop

16. Auditorium and stage

17. Daily school routine and maintenance of buildings and grounds

18. Street and highway safety

19. School bus

20. School policies in regard to safety

21. Safety education and community relations

Evaluative criteria against which to assess the school plant may also be used in appraising recreational areas since many of them are similar to, or identical with, the school plant.

When the check list is obtained, or constructed if this is more desirable for the particular situation, survey procedures are used for collecting information on the present conditions of the plant (4, 15). This may be done by school personnel, by the research bureau of the state or of a university in the area or by survey specialists employed by the school district for this purpose. Since the success of the survey depends primarily upon the willingness of the school staff and the community to implement the findings, these people should have a significant role in such an appraisal. If an outside agency assumes the responsibility for conducting the survey, it is essential that the cooperation and approval of the school staff and community be obtained beforehand.

Data-gathering techniques include the questionnaire, interview, check lists and rating scales. Questionnaires and interviews are used when information is sought directly from an individual. The questionnaire is a form which is usually sent through the mail requesting factual information from the respondent.

Constructing the questionnaire. If it is necessary to collect information from a number of individuals during the process of surveying the school plant, the questionnaire may be a useful device for gathering such data. Questionnaires are time-saving as compared to the interview in that any number of individuals may be queried within a short period of time. Questionnaire construction, however, is not a simple matter, "but requires time, patience, ingenuity, and skill." [1]

Before using the questionnaire the investigator should be certain that the answers are not available in written form, such as records, reports or documents. He should also be sure that the recipients of the questionnaire have the information requested readily accessible. The investigator may find that he has few respondents to his questionnaires, if it is necessary for the recipients to do research in order to provide the answers.

Criteria for constructing questionnaires include:

1. Does each item ask for pertinent information?

2. Are items short, concise and clearly stated?

3. Do items ask for factual information rather than expression of opinion?

4. Can each item be answered easily and briefly by checking the chosen response or by writing a word, phrase or short statement?

5. When the categorical (check list) question is used, do the possible responses include all of the desired information?

6. Are questions interesting and appealing to the respondent?

7. Do the questions avoid antagonizing or embarrassing the respondent?

8. Are responses easily tabulated for data analysis?

9. Will the data collected from the questionnaire answer the problem which is being investigated?

10. Is the questionnaire comprehensive enough to answer the problem, yet short enough to encourage response?

11. Does a letter of transmittal accompany the questionnaire describing the purpose of the study and requesting cooperation?

12. Do items avoid proliferation and overlapping?

Questionnaires which are concerned with opinions, attitudes or interests are called *opinionnaires, attitude inventories,* and *interest inventories.* The open-end (free response) question is frequently used for

[1] Carter V. Good, *Introduction to Educational Research* (New York: Appleton-Century-Crofts, Inc., 1959), p. 191.

eliciting such information since it may go beyond strictly factual material and provide information about feelings.

The interview is used when face-to-face communication is necessary. When the interview is used for research purposes rather than as a counseling instrument, questions are prepared in advance and a recording system is devised for collecting the responses of the interviewee. Questions may be unstructured or highly structured depending upon the problem to be answered.

Check lists and rating scales. Such appraisal tools as check lists and rating scales are those most frequently used in assessing the school plant or recreational area. Check lists include items which are checked according to whether or not they are present in the situation, usually under "yes" or "no" categories. An illustration follows in which the criterion is first stated and is followed by the check list:

	Yes	*No*
16.[2] Slippery, splintered, or dirty treads on stairways are hazardous.		
Treads of stairways are non-skid	_____	_____
The treads are in good condition	_____	_____

An example of another check list which uses a slightly different format follows:

In Our Community[3]	*Yes*	*No*	*Recommended Practice*
Beaches and shoreline areas,	_____	_____	(1) Easily accessible
if available, are:	_____	_____	(2) Lifeguards on duty at specified periods
	_____	_____	(3) Boating facilities available

The rating scale is similar to the check list but includes descriptions of the degree of quality of the factor being appraised. If so desired, a

[2] California State Department of Education, *Check List for a Healthful and Safe School Environment* (Sacramento: State Department of Education, 1957), p. 6.
[3] State of California Recreation Commission, *A Check List for Public Recreation Services in California Communities* (Sacramento: State Recreation Commission, August, 1955), p. 3.

numerical value may be assigned to each rating category for scoring purposes. An example of a rating scale:

Yes   Partly   No

102.[4] All attic and basement rooms
under stairways are kept clean   ____   ____   ____

When the survey data are collected, they are carefully tabulated and organized so that specific needs are identified. The results are based upon objective evidence and are interpreted without bias. Recommendations are made for implementing the results with a carefully considered plan of action spelled out.

Selected References

1. Anderson, Harold H. (Ed.), *Creativity and Its Cultivation*. New York: Harper & Brothers, 1959.

2. California State Department of Education, *Check List for a Healthful and Safe School Environment*. Sacramento: State Department of Education, 1957.

3. Combs, Arthur W. and Donald Snygg, *Individual Behavior*, Rev. Ed. New York: Harper & Brothers, 1959.

4. Good, Carter V., *Introduction to Educational Research*. New York: Appleton-Century-Crofts, Inc., 1959.

5. Gordon, Ira J., *The Teacher As a Guidance Worker*. New York: Harper & Brothers, 1956.

6. Joint Committee on Health Problems in Education of the National Education Association and the American Medical Association, *Healthful School Living*. Washington, D.C.: National Education Association, 1957.

7. Moustakas, C. E. (Ed.), *The Self*. New York: Harper & Brothers, 1956.

8. Murphy, Gardner, *Human Potentialities*. New York: Basic Books, Inc., 1957.

9. National Commission on Safety Education of the National Education Association, *Checklist of Safety and Safety Education in Your School*. Washington, D.C.: National Education Association, 1953.

---

[4] National Commission on Safety Education of the National Education Association, *Checklist of Safety and Safety Education in Your School* (Washington, D.C.: National Education Association, 1953), p. 17.

10. National Recreation Association, *Schedule for the Appraisal of Community Recreation*, Rev. Ed. New York: National Recreation Association, 1951.

11. National Study of Secondary School Evaluation, *Evaluative Criteria*. Washington, D.C.: National Education Association, 1960.

12. Prescott, Daniel A. (Chairman, A Report of the Committee on the Relation of Emotion to the Educative Process), *Emotion and the Educative Process*. Washington, D.C.: American Council on Education, 1938.

13. State of California Recreation Commission, *A Check List for Public Recreation Services in California Communities*, Publication 55-1. Sacramento, 14: State Recreation Commission, August, 1955.

14. Strang, Ruth, *The Role of the Teacher in Personnel Work*, 4th Ed. New York: Bureau of Publications, Teachers College, Columbia University, 1953.

15. Strayer, George D., Jr., *Planning for School Surveys*, Bulletin of the School of Education, Indiana University, Vol. 24, No. 2. Bloomington: Division of Research and Field Services, Indiana University, 1948.

16. The National Facilities Conference, *A Guide for Planning Facilities for Athletics, Recreation, Physical and Health Education*. Chicago: The Athletic Institute, 1947.

7

EVALUATING THE CLIMATE

EVALUATION COMPETENCIES

To understand:

1. the criteria for evaluating climate
2. how to evaluate the teacher or leader
3. how to evaluate instruction

EXPERIENCES FOR THE STUDENT

1. Evaluate the "climate" in your own classroom or playground, using the check lists included in this chapter. Interpret the results and make suggestions for implementing them.
2. Construct your own check list and evaluate the "climate" of your own class or of another class:
   a. Select and describe the principles you are interested in implementing;
   b. Construct items which will indicate the degree of implementation;
   c. Evaluate the data and make suggestions for improving implementation of the principles.

The climate in the educational or recreational situation is the responsibility of the person in charge, the teacher or leader. It is affected by the teacher's relationship to the students or by the leader's relationship to the participants. As has been previously stressed in this book, it is essential for the teacher or leader to *know* the individuals with whom he is working in order to help them find worthwhile experiences.

Jersild,[1] in his discussion of teachers' aspirations and problems, makes the following statement: "To have insight into the child's strivings and the problems he faces, the teacher must strive to face the same problems within his own life." He further describes the strong effect of the teacher's actions on the child's feeling of his own worth and emphasizes

---

[1] Arthur T. Jersild, *When Teachers Face Themselves* (New York: Bureau of Publications, Teachers College, Columbia University, 1955), p. 82.

the fact that the teacher should *know himself* that he might be better able to work with students.

Waller[2] states that the teacher personality is produced by the student-teacher relationship, which he describes as ". . . a special form of dominance and subordination . . ." and further implies that this personality is characterized by inflexibility, lack of creativity and insecurity based on fear.

It would follow that teachers and leaders who are fearful, didactic and non-inventive would be capable of providing only an atmosphere of a similar type, stifling to participants and leader alike.

The first step, then, is for the teacher or leader to understand himself and the climate he is producing. He needs to evaluate his practices in working with others whom he is presumably guiding. A hostile and cruel teacher or leader who invites failure in others may further retard the development of the child with unhealthy self concepts. "Even if a child's self has developed healthily in a happy home atmosphere, a teacher who is harsh and unsympathetic may interfere with the process of healthy development." [3]

Developing an instrument for the evaluation of the teacher or leader first requires a definition of the leader's purpose. If the only goal of a teacher is to stimulate rote learning, tests which evaluate rote learning in students would be used to determine if the goal were accomplished. There are undoubtedly educational institutions where this is the only goal and in such institutions objective knowledge examinations and academic achievement ratings would be used to evaluate the worth of the instructor. In such institutions the instructor who consistently produced students who rated highest in such examinations would be ranked as a superior teacher by his administration.

If the goal of a recreation leader is to have a large number of participants each day, the worth of the leader may readily be determined by counting the daily number of participants.

Goals which provide for the healthy growth and development of individuals in our culture must include democratic values. School and recreation programs may well have numerous goals for the best growth

[2] Willard Waller, "What Teaching Does to Teachers (Part c. The Encircled Mind), in *Identity and Anxiety* edited by Maurice Stein, Arthur J. Vidich, and David Manning White (Glencoe, Ill.: The Free Press, 1960), p. 334.

[3] Arthur T. Jersild, *In Search of Self* (New York: Bureau of Publications, Teachers College, Columbia University, 1952), p. 94.

and development of children and youth. These specific goals should be stated and values should be determined against which to evaluate. If a goal of a school or a recreation program is to stimulate the development of individuals competent to live productively in a democratic society, then tools should be used to appraise student competence in democratic skills as a measure of the instructor's worth as a teacher or leader.

A democratic climate is necessary for the learning of democratic skills, and, as has been previously stated, the teacher or leader is primary in the climate-setting.

Criteria for Evaluating Climate

Each individual is unique, is different from other individuals. He must be given the freedom to be different. Groups are formed when individuals join together with a common purpose. Within the group structure each individual should maintain his uniqueness, directing it productively toward the solution of the group goal. Group cooperation would then be shared activity for the mutual benefit of all group members. It should not imply the loss of individuality but the enhancement of individuality through cooperative efforts with other individuals in reaching mutual goals. Anderson (1) terms such group effort "social development" in contrast to "socialization." He further defines social development as comprising "self-respect, self-production, and respect for the individuality and dignity of others. It requires two-way communication and excludes the negative relationships of cultural domination as in the use of force, threat, and guilt. . . . In this kind of relationship there is no limit to one's creativity or social development." [4]

Socialization is described by Anderson as the concept of conforming to the culture with a stifling of creativity and originality, a sublimation of the individual to the cultural demands. (1)

Values, therefore, derived from the democratic philosophy for the best *social development* of the individual in a democracy include:

1. The individual must feel his own worth. He must respect the worth of others. He must believe that the human personality represents the highest value. He must live in fraternity with his fellows. He must care about each human being.

[4] Harold H. Anderson, "Creativity as Personality Development" in *Creativity and Its Cultivation* edited by Harold H. Anderson (New York: Harper & Brothers, 1959), p. 137.

2. The individual must be able to act on thinking. He must be able to make decisions based on value.

3. The individual must be able to be inquiring, experimental, creative. He must be capable of contributing to and participating in a changing world.

4. The individual must be able to assume responsibility for his own welfare and assist in assuming responsibility for the welfare of others.

5. The individual must be able to participate cooperatively in group life. He must be able to work with others for the common good.

How to Evaluate the Teacher or Leader

A non-threatening atmosphere is essential to encourage the unfolding of creativity, of experimentalism, of healthy growth and development in the United States (1, 3, 4, 7, 8). Since the teacher or leader is responsible for the climate-setting, it follows that appraisal of the teacher or leader is an important factor in evaluating environments.

A check list which may be used by a teacher or leader in evaluating his own behavior is given as an illustration.

Leader's Self Evaluation

Purpose: 1. To help the leader identify his behaviors in working with others
2. To help the leader identify personal qualities which need to be improved

Value Statements	Leader Behaviors	I do this	I need to improve
1. Each individual has worth and dignity.	1.1 I use techniques to find out about each person with whom I work	____	____
	1.2 I provide experiences to meet the needs and interests of each person in the group	____	____
	1.3 I respect the right of each person to be different		

	I do *this*	*I need to* *improve*

and I try to help each one grow in his own way

1.4 I am courteous and kind to each person rather than sarcastic or punishing

1.5 I am sincerely interested in each person, not in just a chosen few

1.6 I can honestly say that I know and like each person in the group:

    1.61 I know each person by name

    1.62 I know something about each person's desires, needs, interests and try to help him meet them

    1.63 I respect each individual as a worthwhile person and show him that I value him as such

2. Each individual has the right to be inquiring and experimental.

2.1 I establish a permissive atmosphere in which creativity is encouraged:

    2.11 I listen to all thoughts and opinions

    2.12 I help each person find resources which stimuate new ideas

    2.13 I accept new ideas and new points of view

    2.14 I provide opportunities for individuals to explore their own particular interests

	I do this	*I need to improve*
2.15 I allow adequate time for the creative process to occur	___	___
2.16 I allow individuals to just sit and think without harassment	___	___
2.17 I encourage diversity rather than conformity	___	___
2.18 I constantly encourage rather than ridicule	___	___
2.2 I am, myself, experimental and inventive:		
2.21 I am constantly trying better ways of working	___	___
2.22 I read new research findings in my field	___	___
2.23 I set up research projects of my own	___	___
2.24 I work and study with professional groups to improve my competencies in leadership	___	___
2.25 I read widely in many areas and try to apply new knowledges to my profession	___	___
2.26 I explore my own unusual avenues of interest and try to extend my perceptions	___	___
2.27 I am able to change with a changing world rather than insisting on doing things as they have always been done	___	___

	I do *this*	*I need to* *improve*

3. Each individual should have the opportunity to work with others for the common good.

3.1 I encourage group planning ____ ____

3.2 I help groups identify common problems and goals ____ ____

3.3 I assist individuals in developing effective group work skills ____ ____

3.4 I try to improve my own group work skills: ____ ____

    3.41 I read new materials in this area ____ ____

    3.42 I participate actively in at least one professional group ____ ____

    3.43 I get resource help to improve my group work skills when it is needed ____ ____

3.5 I carefully plan group experiences where boys and girls can work on their developmental tasks:

    3.51 I am aware of the developmental tasks for children and youth ____ ____

    3.52 I have identified particular tasks that individuals in my group are working on ____ ____

    3.53 I am patient with individuals and groups who have difficulties and try to help them improve ____ ____

4. Each individual should make decisions based on value.

4.1 I encourage individuals to make their own decisions ____ ____

4.2 I use a problem solving

	I do *this*	*I need to* *improve*

method in working with individuals:

    4.21 I help individuals develop and use value statements

    4.22 I help individuals learn how to identify and solve problems, evaluating results against predetermined values

    4.23 I solve my own problems in an orderly way, measuring the results against value

4.3 I avoid making "snap" decisions and I state the values used in making a decision

4.4 I help each individual assess his own progress rather than measuring him against group norms

4.5 I help individuals reevaluate decisions which are open to question, whether made by me or by them:

    4.51 I help individuals recognize that poor decisions should not be enforced but should be changed

    4.52 I help individuals understand that under different circumstances decisions may need to be altered and should be constantly re-evaluated

How to Evaluate Instruction

Numerous studies have been done for the purpose of assessing teaching effectiveness (2, 5, 6, 9). One aspect of teaching effectiveness concerns instructional procedures. Such procedures or methodology affect climate. For example, a methodology which places a premium on memorizing information de-emphasizes critical thinking and problem solving which in turn limits inquiry and experimentalism.

The first step in evaluating instruction is to define the principles which describe the instructional procedures for attaining the goals. For example, the uniqueness of each individual is valued in a democracy. The principle related to this may be, "Best learning occurs when there is opportunity for individuals to progress according to their own goals, interests, and abilities."

The next step in developing the instrument is to determine the instructional procedures which would implement the principle. The best technique for collecting the data, such as a rating scale, questionnaire or check list, is selected and constructed.

Such a check list for rating instruction is given as an illustration. The principles used in developing this check list were selected from the foundation facts for the healthy growth and development of the individual.

Check List for Appraising Instruction

Purpose: 1. To identify areas where principles are not in operation
2. To evaluate climate by assessing instructional procedures

Directions to the student: Check your response to each item in the appropriate space. Under comments write any suggestions you have for improving the application of the particular principle.

YES   NO   I. PURPOSE: The group goals must be the purposes of the individuals who comprise the group.

_____   _____   1. My individual goals were included in the group goals.

_____   _____   2. I feel that I was capable of deciding what should be done in the group.

_____ _____   3. The help given by the instructor in choosing and setting up the group undertakings was adequate.

Comment:

PURPOSE: Purposes must be clearly defined so that procedures for attaining the purposes may be readily determined.

_____ _____   4. I felt that my goals were well clarified.

_____ _____   5. The goals I set seemed important to me.

_____ _____   6. I had a definite feeling of purpose, of a problem to be solved.

7. I had a feeling of purpose
   _____ only when I was directly responsible.
   _____ most of the time.
   _____ very little of the time.

Comment:

YES   NO   II. EXPERIENCES: The experiences must be so closely related to the purposes that purpose and experience are inseparable.

_____ _____   8. My goals, problems and needs were met by the course experiences.

_____ _____   9. I had an opportunity to achieve my goals in any way I was resourceful enough to figure out.

_____ _____   10. I did use many different resources to solve my problems.

_____ _____   11. I felt confident and happy in exploring new ideas.

EXPERIENCES: Experiences should extend the personal world of the individual.

_____ _____   12. I gained new ideas from this class.

____   ____   13. I developed new interests in this class which I wish to explore further.

Comment:

YES   NO   III. INDIVIDUAL DEVELOPMENT: An individual should have the opportunity to achieve his own goals irrespective of group goals.

____   ____   14. I feel that I had an opportunity to do my own learning in my own way and to conduct my own experiences in relation to my goals.

____   ____   15. I took advantage of the opportunity to do my own learning in my own way.

____   ____   16. In solving group problems many of my individual goals were achieved.

Comment:

YES   NO   IV. SOCIAL DEVELOPMENT: An individual should have opportunity to participate with other individuals in achieving common goals.

____   ____   17. I feel that the group participated actively in solving group problems.

____   ____   18. I made a sincere effort to help others in the group.

____   ____   19. The atmosphere in the group made it easy for me to express opinions.

____   ____   20. Each person with whom I worked was kind and considerate.

____   ____   21. I feel that I had ample opportunity to assume leadership responsibilities.

Comment:

YES   NO   V. ORGANIZATION: Organization and progression of experiences should proceed hand-in-hand with individual development.

_____   _____   22. Techniques were used to help me find where I was in relation to the course experiences.

_____   _____   23. I felt my course experiences began where I was.

_____   _____   24. The materials in the course were set up in such a way that I could understand what was happening.

_____   _____   25. The sequence of experiences was reorganized whenever necessary for better understanding.

Comment:

YES   NO   VI. EVALUATION: Evaluation should be used to determine and clarify purposes and to appraise progress in goal achievement.

_____   _____   26. I evaluated my achievement in relation to my own goals.

_____   _____   27. I evaluated my achievement in relation to the group goals.

_____   _____   28. I evaluated my achievement with the instructor in such a way that it was possible for me to continue progressing.

_____   _____   29. I made an effort to extend my experiences as a result of the evaluation procedures.

_____   _____   30. In the process of achieving old goals, I have set new goals to work on.

Comment:

Selected References

1. Anderson, Harold H. (Ed.), *Creativity and Its Cultivation.* New York: Harper & Brothers, 1959.

2. Leiderman, Gloria F., Thomas L. Hilton, and Harry Levin, "Studies of Teachers' Behavior: A Summary Report," *Journal of Teacher Education,* Vol. 8, December, 1957, pp. 433-37.

3. Jersild, Arthur T., *In Search of Self*. New York: Bureau of Publications, Teachers College, Columbia University, 1952.

4. ———, *When Teachers Face Themselves*. New York: Bureau of Publications, Teachers College, Columbia University, 1955.

5. Long, Sister Mary, "A Synthesis of Recent Research Studies on Predicting Teaching Efficiency," *Catholic Educational Review*, Vol. 55, April, 1957, pp. 217-30.

6. Mitzel, Harold E., *A Behavioral Approach to the Assessment of Teacher Effectiveness*. New York: Office of Research and Evaluation, Division of Teacher Education (535 East 80th Street), February, 1957.

7. Smith, Paul (Ed.), *Creativity: An Examination of the Creative Process*. New York: Hastings House, 1959.

8. Stein, Morris I. and Shirley J. Heinze, *Creativity and the Individual*. Glencoe, Illinois: The Free Press, 1960.

9. Tomlinson, Loren R., "Recent Studies in the Evaluation of Teaching," *Educational Research Bulletin* 34, October, 1955, pp. 172-86.

10. Stein, Maurice, Arthur J. Vidich, and David Manning White (Ed.), *Identity and Anxiety*. Glencoe, Illinois: The Free Press, 1960.

11. Wiles, Kimball, Camille Brown, and Rosalind Cassidy, *Supervision in Physical Education*. Englewood Cliffs, N. J.: Prentice-Hall, Inc., 1956.

8

MARKING AND GRADING

EVALUATION COMPETENCIES

To *understand:*

1. *marking and grading as a communication technique*
2. *the reasons for perpetuating the traditional marking system*
3. *the teacher's role in improving communication and in minimizing the negative effects of marking and grading*

EXPERIENCES FOR THE STUDENT

1. *Study the marking and grading system of a particular institution. Make recommendations for: (a) improving communication; (b) minimizing the negative effects.*
2. *Discuss with the administrative personnel of the institution ways and means of improving the system.*

A mark or grade is a code for reporting and recording student achievement. Special attention is given to marking and grading in this book because the authors believe that it is the greatest single problem in education today. Marking is confused with evaluation and the mark frequently becomes the primary goal toward which the student is working. The mark controls the teacher as well as the student as the real meaning of education becomes clouded in the unreality of a code and the mark becomes the value against which goals are evaluated. Parents, teachers and students focus on the code as a measure of student success.

If grades or marks were done away with, students, teachers and parents would be forced to face the fact that education should be focused on learning, and that learning takes place in relation to student purposes. Evaluation tools would be used to help students define purposes and appropriate experiences for fulfilling the purposes would be provided.

The value placed upon an individual by other persons is a strong influence on how he develops. Within our present educational system from the kindergarten through the university the grade or mark has become to the student an expression of the value placed upon him by the teacher and the school. He feels valued or not valued through the mark.

An understanding of the marking system as it is used today in the schools may help the teacher clarify guidelines for working more effectively in the structure.

Marking and Grading as Communication

The mark or grade in education is used as an instrument of communication. The code which is used in most school systems signifies "best" or "superior" with the letter "A" and continues through the alphabet to "F" which stands for "failure."

Communication of educational achievement is necessary between (a) the teacher and student, (b) the teacher and the student's parent, (c) the teacher and the school which is attended by the student and (d) between educational institutions attended by the student.

The most effective procedure for teacher-student and teacher-parent communication is face-to-face discussion utilizing the conference or interview technique. Another possibility if the conference is not feasible is a written report which describes specifically the goals being worked on, the individual accomplishment of the goals and a statement of the next steps to be achieved. The least effective technique is a code which uses a single mark or grade to describe accomplishment in a broad subject matter area.

The teacher-school and school-school communication is a one-way process which precludes face-to-face discussion and must be done by a written report of some nature.

Teacher-student communication. The teacher needs to be competent in helping the student evaluate goal achievement. This process includes: (a) the identification of individual goals, utilizing the tools and procedures for understanding the individual's status, practices and motives which are reflections of his self; (b) determining where the individual is in relation to the goals by using status measures; (c) selecting experiences for goal fulfillment; and (d) assessing progress toward goal achievement with the resulting identification of new goals. A mark or grade is immaterial to the success of such a teaching-learning situation and may actually inhibit best learning by threatening or re-warding the student with an unrelated totem.

The highest level of communication, therefore, between the teacher and student is that achieved through such an evaluation process. Mark-ing and grading, as an effective evaluation procedure, would receive an "F" for failure as described by its own code.

Teacher-parent communication. The parent should understand the specific goals being worked on and the student's achievement in relation to the goals. He should also understand how the home and school can work together to best accomplish those goals which are essential to the healthy growth and development of his child.

The teacher who cares about his pupils is vitally concerned with each one developing in his own best way. If the teacher could report to the parent without the interference of marks or grades, he would be better able to communicate these understandings through the results of the student-teacher evaluations.

The parent usually aspires for his child something better than what he is or has. He hopes that his child will be successful in the elementary school, the secondary school, the college or university. In the eyes of most parents success in school is described by the student's marks, a distortion which prevents the parent from undertanding what his child is actually trying to do and where he is in goal achievement. More effective communication is needed between school and home than is possible with the present grade report, and it is inevitable that this will go hand-in-hand with improved teacher-student communication.

Teacher-school communication. A school or college which over the years is concerned with thousands, even millions of students must have a record of each student's achievement in the particular school objec-tives. Such a record should be concise and clearly descriptive of student accomplishment. In the college or university such a report should in-dicate whether the student is able to profit by the educational experi-ences provided by the institution or whether his education in this school should be terminated. In the public school such a report would indicate student progress from year to year.

When reporting to the school or university, the teacher should de-scribe student achievement in a particular, identifiable goal which is accepted by the institution as the subject matter of the course and which may be accurately interpreted by the institution. For example, if the institution considers physical education to be the knowledges and skills in human movement, the report should indicate the student's achievement in this subject matter and should *not* be based on the student's attitudes, habits and showering and dressing accomplishments.

It is discouraging to observe that in many schools a large percentage of the physical education grade is based upon dressing or stripping and showering. When a demerit system is used, a student who fails to dress or shower several times may receive a failure in physical education. In addition to this, he may also receive a low mark in character traits which may include cooperation, work habits, attitude and participation all because he did not dress according to a required standard. Some marking systems become so elaborate in this respect that points are subtracted for a dirty blouse or for not wearing gym sox. It is disconcerting to discover that much of the subject matter of physical education, if the grading practices are any criteria, is apparently that of teaching students to dress according to a standard and to shower at the end of each physical education period.

Many of the deplorable marking habits which teachers have developed, however, are the result of the need for protection against criticism of parents, students and administrators. It is difficult for a parent or student to argue about the mark if it may be substantiated by the exact number of showers taken, the attendance record and similar specific points. Many teachers feel more secure when they are using such a system and it apparently never occurs to either parents or students to question the criteria.

It would seem that a better reporting system could be devised than the present grading and marking code. The health record of the individual, for example, indicates very clearly his status in specific conditions without assigning a grade to his heart murmur or his scoliosis.

Whatever reporting system is used, it should include a precise description of student achievement in well-defined educational goals.

School-school communication.   As in teacher-school communication, records should be reported concisely and should be readily interpreted by the educational institution receiving them. The same problems of communication are present in reporting from one educational institution to another as are present in reporting from teacher to school.

The present grading and marking system leaves much to be desired in this respect as an "A" in one institution may very well be equivalent to a "D" in another institution, and the subject matter in health education in one institution may be entirely different from the course similarly titled in another school or college. A precise description of the course experiences with student achievement indicated through the use of evaluation techniques could improve the situation. Certainly further careful study of this problem is indicated.

Reasons for Perpetuating the Present Marking System

In a discussion of the present marking and grading system Snygg and Combs state:[5] "We cannot afford to write off one-half or more of our population by persuading them that they are failures. There is good reason to believe that our competitive marking system is doing just this and that it should be abandoned."

Why, then, do the schools insist upon perpetuating the present outmoded marking and grading system?

The marking system may be perpetuated by the parents. The parent needs to feel secure in his relationship to his child's school. He does not wish to be put into a situation where he feels inadequate. He wishes to retain that with which he is familiar, and he is familiar with the traditional marking system for in his own educational background he has been marked and graded. This reporting system also permits him to avoid any personal contact with his child's school. He simply signs the report card and admonishes or praises his child as the case may be.

If, however, the teacher requests a conference with him to discuss his child's achievement, he may be fearful that he will be put into a situation of admitting that his child is inadequate. If such is the case, he may also feel inadequate. In addition, he may be asked to have a conference with a high school teacher when he himself may have terminated his education after the eighth grade. This may be very threatening to him and it is understandable that a parent insists upon the familiar reporting system in which a code is sent to him for signature.

For the successful parent with the adequate child the parent-teacher conference would be very satisfactory. But for the parent who feels inadequate and fears that his child is also inadequate, this system of facing a teacher in conference may be terrorizing to the parent.

[5] Donald Snygg and Arthur W. Combs, *Individual Behavior* (New York: Harper & Brothers, 1949), p. 223.

Under such circumstances it is imperative that the teacher-student relationship be one in which the student does not feel threatened. When the teacher knows and likes the student, he is able to reassure the student, and consequently the parent, even though the student may be having difficulty in accomplishing the goals set by the school. It is very difficult for a teacher who *knows* a student to also dislike him. The parent-teacher conference then becomes a sharing of ideas in determining how best to help the student achieve his goals.

The marking system may be perpetuated by the teacher. The inadequate teacher needs the marking system as a crutch for the purpose of (*a*) maintaining control over students, (*b*) forcing students to work on the teacher's goal which they might otherwise refuse to do, (*c*) avoiding the clarification of student goals and experiences, (*d*) satisfying his own hostility by punishing students and (*e*) preventing the student, parent and school from discovering his inadequacies in the use of the evaluation process.

As long as curriculum offerings are meaningless to students, outside motivations are necessary to force them to work. If the school has set requirements which the student must meet but which are unrelated to his particular needs or interests, the grade serves as an external motivation to force the student to do something which he would not do otherwise. In such a situation the grade becomes a punitive measure to coerce the student to do what the school and/or the teacher thinks he should do. This system, unfortunately, functions in most of our educational institutions today.

The traditional marking system is used in health education and physical education. The recreation program has thus far escaped the hazards of grading and marking.

Physical education and health education personnel are themselves responsible for their own dilemma. They have insisted that they receive academic respectability by using the marking system which is used in other school subjects. As a result, at the present time practically every educational institution in the country assigns physical education grades and health education grades on the same "A to F" scale which is used in assigning grades in other school subjects.

Grading and marking is detrimental enough in other school subjects which are primarily concerned with the cognitive area, the recall of subject matter knowledges and intellectual development. But in physical education and health education, assigning grades and marks is disastrous.

The goals and experiences of health education and physical education are centered on the healthy growth and development of the individual. Grading and marking may seriously inhibit the achievement of such goals.

The marking system may be perpetuated by the student. To some students the mark has become a symbol of external control and they are comfortable in the situation. To eliminate the mark or grade would force the student to develop inner control over his situation by setting his own goals and assuming responsibility for his own learning. The grade has become the most significant valuing process in his educational life.

The student desires to achieve his potentialities. If the subject matter included in the school courses is related to his own goals, he is eager to attain it and the grade or mark may be irrelevant. If the educational goals are not those which help him achieve his potentialities, he works on his own goals outside of the educational demands and his educational goal becomes grade achievement. When such is the case the usual query of the student to the teacher is, "What do *you* want?" and when the student is unsuccessful in obtaining an "A" his defense is usually, "I didn't know what *he* (the teacher) wanted."

Under such circumstances students may feel that the end justifies the means and any tactics for achievement of the "A" are acceptable, and are frequently used.

If a student's *primary* incentive is to achieve his own potentialities and attain his own particular aspirations through the educational experiences, if he is truly inner directed, an external mark or grade will be of much less concern to him.

The marking system may be perpetuated by institutions. Educational institutions reflect the culture. When parents, teachers and students favor the retention of the marking and grading system those in charge of such decisions in the schools and colleges may hesitate to suggest changes.

Those in leadership roles should contribute to the advancement of learning by improving the learning conditions. It is easier to continue procedures which have been in effect than to experiment with new ideas and face the disapproval of those who wish to retain the old. Courageous leadership in the public schools, in colleges and universities would do much to implement more effective reporting procedures.

The Teacher's Role in Improving Communication and Minimizing the Negative Effects of Marking and Grading

The teacher who is required to use a mark or grade in reporting student achievement may minimize the deleterious effects of the grade by: (a) making it clear to the student that the mark does *not* represent teacher valuing of him and *only* represents his achievement as measured by a group standard or norm; (b) helping the student understand that his individual goal achievement must take precedence over the external goal as represented by the grade; (c) helping the student evaluate his goal achievement according to his individual progress rather than emphasizing group standards; and (d) making every effort to provide a curriculum which provides experiences for meeting student's individual goals.

In reporting to the parent and to the school, the teacher should describe as accurately as possible the achievement of the student in a specific educational area. He should use two-way communication with the parent whenever possible to clarify the specific goals being worked on and the student's progress in accomplishing the goals. This procedure alone would help many physical education teachers improve their grading criteria.

In reporting to the school, the teacher should understand the precise meaning attached to each of the symbols in the code and the subject matter of his course as described by the school so that his report may provide the institution with an accurate picture of student progress in goal achievement.

Teachers whose chief concerns are with students rather than grades will help students, parents and school administrators move a step further toward intelligent evaluation and communication of student achievement.

Selected References

1. Association for Supervision and Curriculum Development, *Reporting Is Communicating*. Washington, D.C.: National Education Association, 1956.

2. Bloom, Benjamin S. (Ed.), *Taxonomy of Educational Objectives*. New York: Longmans, Green and Co., 1956.

3. Langdon, Grace and Irving M. Stout, *Teacher-Parent Interviews*. Engle-wood Cliffs, N.J.: Prentice-Hall, Inc., 1954.

4. Snygg, Donald and Arthur W. Combs, *Individual Behavior*. New York: Harper & Brothers, 1949.

PART FOUR

Finding out about THE EXPERIENCES

Competencies Needed By Teachers and Leaders in Health Education, Physical Education and Recreation

1. To understand the evaluation of experiences

2. To understand the evaluation of movement skills in sports, dance and aquatics

3. To understand the evaluation of subject matter knowledges

4. To understand the evaluation of programs

Objective	Value or Criterion	Measuring Tool
To understand the evaluation of experiences	Subject matter in health education, physical education and recreation contributing to healthy growth and development of the individual	None
To appraise movement skills in sports, dance and aquatics	Predetermined standards for skill performance in sports, dance and aquatics	Rating scales Check lists Skill tests
To evaluate subject matter knowledges	Knowledges in health education, physical education and recreation	Essay examination Written objective examination
To evaluate programs in health education, physical education and recreation	Healthy growth and development of the individual in contemporary United States	Check lists Rating scales

9

THE EVALUATION OF EXPERIENCES

EVALUATION COMPETENCIES

To understand:
1. *how to evaluate learning experiences which have predetermined standards*
2. *how to evaluate learning experiences which have no predetermined standards*

EXPERIENCES FOR THE STUDENT

1. *Select (or construct) an instrument for evaluating an experience with predetermined standards. Administer the instrument to a group of classmates and interpret the data.*
2. *Engage in a creative experience of some nature and evaluate yourself, describing the criteria you have used in the evaluative process.*

Evaluation is indeed a part and parcel of teaching. All of the evaluation procedures described in this book are in some way educational experiences for the student.

Part Two of this book describes ways in which the teacher may better understand the student so that he may help the student identify his real goals and problems. Procedures for identifying pupil purpose and pupil need should be used early in the educational experience. The identification of such need, problems, attitudes, purposes, interests is an essential part of the educational program and of the education of the student. Many of the learning experiences for the student in health education, physical education and recreation are directly within the area of understanding the student.

Other fields of education such as history, English, mathematics may use procedures for finding student needs and purposes in order that they may better relate their course subject matter to the student. In the fields of health education, physical education and recreation the procedures for understanding the student may also be the course subject matter. For example, a knowledge examination may actually be given on the procedures used in the health examination to find out whether or not the student understands the function of the health examination in his own healthy growth and development. Thus, the experiences described in Part Two are not only participated in by the students but they are studied as subject matter understandings.

In Part Three ways are suggested for evaluating environments against criteria which are conducive to healthy growth and development. The students may participate with teachers or leaders in evaluating these environments and in determining how to improve environmental conditions. Part Three, therefore, may be considered to be subject matter experiences for helping in student development in health education, physical education and recreation. For example, students may undertake a project to survey school sanitary facilities, identify problems and make recommendations for improvement to administrative officers. A group of students may study the effect of marking or grading on setting goals, study how this affects healthy growth and development and make suggestions for solving such health problems.

The materials to be considered in Part Four deal with ways of evaluating subject matter experiences which are used to help individuals in goal accomplishment. When an individual has identified a problem (a concern, intention, question, goal, fault or difficulty), he then selects experiences which will help him to solve the problem. These experiences may help him solve personal problems, such as "I want to improve my posture so I will be more attractive," or they may be experiences which help to solve community or group problems, such as "How we can improve the recreational opportunities in the community," or "I want to learn basketball so I can play with my friends."

The subject matter experiences in health education, physical education and recreation must first be evaluated according to how well they meet individual goals and objectives of the participants. These experiences may be (a) sports, dance and aquatics experiences which have a composition of predetermined objectives and standards, (b) experiences which have no predetermined composition, (c) movement skills used in sports, dance and aquatics and (d) subject matter knowledges.

When the particular subject matter for meeting student objectives has been determined, the next step is to find out where the student is in relation to the subject matter he wishes to learn. The criteria to be used in the evaluation of student achievement in the subject matter experience depend upon whether the experience has a predetermined composition as in the game of basketball or whether it does not have a predetermined composition as in creative dance.

How to Evaluate Learning Experiences Which Have Predetermined Standards

Experiences with predetermined standards may be a sport such as basketball, a folk dance or an aquatics event. The values or criteria against which to evaluate achievement in these experiences are the standards and rules of the activity. These criteria are modified according to the student's personal goals. For example, one student may wish to learn tennis so he may play with his friends, but when he has accomplished this, he may no longer be interested in studying tennis. He may, of course, set new goals while he is studying tennis and he may continue to work until he has won the city tennis tournament. Evaluation in an activity is dependent upon the goals a person brings to it or sets up within it. The person who is playing for recreation may not set as high standards of excellence for himself as the student who is trying to enter intercollegiate competition.

Movement experiences with predetermined standards and objectives include the wide range of sports and dances which make up much of physical education and recreation in the United States today. Each of these activities has a unique composition of its own. Evaluation should be used to find out where the individual is in his understandings and performance of the activity, and where he is in relation to the particular parts of the whole activity or composition.

A teacher or leader may help a student identify where he is in relation to the predetermined standards or objectives of the activity which he desires or needs to accomplish to be or do what he wishes. Such evaluation would be external evaluation, that done by someone other than the person being evaluated, and internal evaluation done by himself. Such mutual sharing of evaluation increases both the teaching and the learning benefits.

At times only external evaluation may be done. It may precede or follow internal evaluation. For best learning, when external evaluation is done, it should be done with the full cooperation of the person being evaluated; it should not be something "done *to* somebody" but should be something "done *for* somebody."

The teacher or leader should be able to help the individual evaluate his performance in the whole activity. He should also be able to identify the various parts which make up the whole and help the individual determine his particular needs in the performance of the activity. An activity is a whole, but unlike an individual, it does have parts and the parts may be measured. Some of the parts which may be studied and measured separately are (*a*) rules, (*b*) equipment, (*c*) terminology, (*d*) player duties, (*e*) strategy, (*f*) team play, (*g*) player positions, (*h*) playing situations, (*i*) sequence of dance figures, (*j*) understanding of music and accompaniment for dance, (*k*) approach for a dive, (*l*) entry into the water, (*m*) performance of specific skills.

How to determine standards of performance against which to evaluate activities. The basic knowledges and skills to be learned for participation in sports, dance and aquatics have been formulated by various organizations throughout the country. These may be the predetermined standards against which the individual is evaluated, the values used in constructing the measuring instruments.

Sources where standards may be obtained include: (*a*) The Division of Girls' and Women's Sports, American Association for Health, Physical Education, and Recreation, Washington 6, D.C., which publishes guides in sports such as softball, tennis, basketball; (*b*) National Federation of State High School Athletic Associations, 7 South Dearborn Street, Chicago, Illinois, which sets up rules for control of interscholastic athletics and rules for sports and athletic events for men and boys; (*c*) The Athletic Institute, Merchandise Mart, Room 805, Chicago 54, Illinois, which publishes guides in all sports events for both men and women; (*d*) state and city courses of study which present local rules and skill standards; (*e*) books which are written for such purposes (*1, 3, 4, 5, 6, 7*).

Sources where standards for dance may be obtained include the many folk dance books describing the specific rules for performing each dance, square dance books and modern dance books describing the criteria for performance in modern dance.

The teacher or leader and participants decide upon the particular standards of performance they wish to achieve and the rules they wish to follow in the activity. These become the values used in constructing the evaluation instruments.

How to Evaluate Learning Experiences Which Have No Predetermined Standards

The creative experience has no predetermined rules, standards or set objectives. The individual has a purpose or intention of his own which he alone understands, and he alone knows when he has fulfilled his intent. If he is able to utilize help from others, he selects what he can use, does his own exploration and experimentation, and he alone knows when he is finished.

Under such circumstances the individual himself is his own judge of his work. Evaluation must be internal. If external criteria are set up and used, the goal is no longer that of creativity.

Internal evaluation can take place when there is no "power over" situation. The individual may take suggestions from the outside, internalize them and use them in a way that makes meaning to him within his own structure. In a school situation a teacher who is marking or grading a student has power over him, and teacher suggestions may block creativity in the student because of this relationship. An example of this is when the teacher evaluates a creative dance which has been composed and performed by the student. External control influences the individual and a really creative act is most difficult to achieve under such conditions. This may be observed in many modern dance classes where the students' movements reflect the movements of the teacher. These students are learning to manage their bodies and to learn techniques of dance from the teacher, but creativity is negligible.

Some of the elements of creativity described in the literature (2, 8) include (*a*) the creative attitude, (*b*) the creative act or process and (*c*) the creative product.

The creative attitude.   The creative attitude has been described as consisting of two parts: (*a*) the elements of creativity in the individual and (*b*) the environment which permits creativity to occur. The elements of creativity in the individual include curiosity, concentration, conflict, flexibility and willingness to experience, spontaneity, expressiveness, anxiety of being alone but ability to withstand ridicule, the desire to communicate the created product, ". . . the willingness to be born every day." [1]

The environment which fosters creativity is described by Rogers[2] as providing two conditions which he terms "psychological safety" and "psychological freedom." A climate which produces psychological safety is one in which the individual is valued as a worthy human being, is

<hr/>

[1] Erich Fromm, "The Creative Attitude," in *Creativity and Its Cultivation,* edited by Harold H. Anderson (New York: Harper & Brothers, 1959), p. 53.

[2] Carl R. Rogers, "Toward a Theory of Creativity," in *Creativity and Its Cultivation,* edited by Harold H. Anderson (New York: Harper & Brothers, 1959), pp. 78-82.

accepted "as of unconditional worth." [3] In this situation there is no external evaluation placed upon either the individual or the creative product and the individual is accepted on his own terms as he sees it, without criticism or reservation. This is what Rogers describes as "understanding empathically." [4]

The creative act.   Some of the aspects of the creative act as described by writers and researchers in the area of creativity are: (*a*) it requires preparation, a steeping of oneself in materials and experiences in the areas in which one wishes to create; (*b*) an insightful occurrence which gives rise to the creative act and during which time the act may be performed; (*c*) conscious or unconscious (or both) perceptions which are part of the creative process; (*d*) time for reflection and introspection.

An evaluation of the creative act or process depends upon the definition. If it is indefinable, external evaluation is impossible. Evaluation would necessarily have to be internal since only the individual would be able to determine the presence of the creative process in himself.

The creative product.   If it is not possible to evaluate the creative person or the creative act externally, it is also impossible to evaluate the creative product using external criteria. Another individual may express his own like or dislike of the product but this is not evaluation against clearly defined, acceptable criteria derived from principles of creativity, and consequently means little.

The only external evaluation possible in appraising creativity consists of evaluating the environment to determine if the factors for fostering creativity are present. Criteria for fostering creativity are included on the check lists for evaluating climate and instruction in Part Three. All other evaluation would need to be internal evaluation by the creator himself. He is the only one who knows his intent, his feeling and his fulfillment of his intent.

The modern dance class, however, may provide possibilities for exploration and for perfecting dance techniques which may free the person to move, making it possible for creativity to arise later when a creative environment permits it. When exploration is taking place the teacher may make any number of suggestions to help the student explore many possibilities for movement. He may help the student apply physiological or mechanical principles in the perfection of dance technique. Under such conditions external criteria may be used to evaluate excellence in

[3] Ibid., p. 78.
[4] Ibid., p. 80.

performance of dance technique and excellence in exploration of movement possibilities. Both teacher and student must be aware of the goal —to learn to use the body well under many conditions. When the creative act is the goal, teacher suggestions, admonitions and evaluations are out of place; the accomplishment of the goal is evaluated only by the creator.

Selected References

1. American Association for Health, Physical Education, and Recreation, *Physical Education for High School Students*. Washington, D.C.: National Education Association, 1955.

2. Anderson, Harold H., (Ed.), *Creativity and Its Cultivation*. New York: Harper & Brothers, 1959.

3. Bresnahan, George T. and W. W. Tuttle, *Track and Field Athletics*, *2nd Ed*. St. Louis: The C. V. Mosby Company, 1947.

4. Meyer, Margaret H. and Marguerite M. Schwarz, *Technic of Team Sports for Women, Rev. Ed*. Philadelphia: W. B. Saunders Company, 1951.

5. Miller, Donna Mae and Katherine L. Ley, *Individual and Team Sports for Women*. Englewood Cliffs, N. J.: Prentice-Hall, Inc., 1955.

6. Seaton, Don Cash, Irene A. Clayton, Howard C. Leibee and Lloyd Messersmith, *Physical Education Handbook, 3rd Ed*. Englewood Cliffs, N. J.: Prentice-Hall, Inc., 1959.

7. Shaw, John H., Carl A. Troester and Milton Gabrielson, *Individual Sports for Men*. Philadelphia: W. B. Saunders Company, 1950.

8. Stein, Morris I. and Shirley J. Heinze, *Creativity and the Individual*. Glencoe, Illinois: The Free Press, 1960.

10

EVALUATION OF MOVEMENT SKILLS IN SPORTS, DANCE AND AQUATICS

EVALUATION COMPETENCIES

To *understand:*

1. how to evaluate total performance within the whole activity
2. how to evaluate movement skills using principles of movement
3. how to evaluate movement skills using standards for performance in the activity

EXPERIENCES FOR THE STUDENT

1. Construct a rating scale or check list for evaluating total performance in a selected activity.
2. Using the principles of movement as criteria for evaluation, construct a check list or rating scale and evaluate a specific skill.
3. Select, administer and interpret a skill test.
4. Construct a skill test and evaluate it against the conditions to be met in constructing such a test.

This chapter is concerned with the evaluation of student achievement in the performance of activity skills. Achievement in total performance within the whole activity may be determined by using rating scales or check lists. These instruments may also be used in assessing "form" using the principles of movement as the values.

Evaluation of movement skills using standards for performance in the activity may be done by using objective skill tests which measure the degree of proficiency in hitting the target, striking the ball or running the bases.

Evaluation of movement skills in sports, dance and aquatics should include all three types of assessment if the student is to have a clear picture of where he is in the activity he wishes to learn.

How to Evaluate Total Performance within the Whole Activity

The rating scale or check list may be used to assess performance in the wholeness of the activity, such as performance in the game of basketball. In determining the ability to play basketball, the values are the combination of factors which describe good performance in basketball. These factors should be described and defined clearly so that all persons who are the external evaluators and all persons being evaluated understand what they are. There must be common agreement on the definition of the trait being measured and the description must be in terms that are understood by all concerned.

For example, in constructing a check list or rating scale to measure ability in playing the game of basketball a description of a good player must be made. Factors to be rated are identified, such as ability to apply knowledge of the rules, playing a given position efficiently, use of effective strategy, desirable team play, proficiency in performance of skills.

After describing the behaviors to be assessed, a check list may be constructed which includes a list of the items to be assessed with columns in which to check the presence or absence of the particular trait. The check list will be discussed more fully in the materials which describe how to evaluate form using movement principles.

In the construction of a rating scale, the behaviors to be rated are described and the type and number of categories are determined and described. Although there are numerous types of rating scales, most of them may be grouped under (*a*) the descriptive type, (*b*) the graphic type and (*c*) the numerical type.

The descriptive type of rating scale. This consists of a number of descriptive phrases arranged in order from the best or most positive behavior to the poorest or most negative behavior. These phrases are set up in check list form and the rater checks the behavior which best describes the person being rated. For example:

Check the phrase which best describes your estimate of the individual's ability to apply knowledge of rules during play.
_____ Consistently avoided infractions of rules
_____ Occasionally showed indecision on how to proceed

_____ Frequently had to be helped in making decisions
_____ Consistently made decisions which caused infractions

The graphic type of rating scale.   This uses short, descriptive phrases or words arranged in order from negative to positive on a continuum. The rater checks the point on the continuum which best describes the degree or quality of the behavior being assessed. The check mark may be placed anywhere along the continuum, between phrases if desired. For example:

Place a check on the line at the point which best describes your estimate of the individual's behavior toward his team-mates during play.

Hostile   Indifferent   Friendly

The numerical type of rating scale.   This scale is the same as the graphic rating scale except that the values along the line are expressed in numbers. It is essential to have the instructions to the rater include a precise description for each numerical category. For example:

RATING OF PERFORMANCE IN BASKETBALL

Name of Player _____   *Rater* _____

To the rater: Check the category which best describes your estimate of the individual's performance in each of the items described.

4—Outstanding performance in all respects; indispensable to the team; correct decisions; used good judgment; absence of error

3—Occasional error but not generally detrimental to play; usually good judgment and correct decisions

2—Needs improvement in some areas; some poor decisions; uncertain at times

1—Many errors; poor judgment; inadequate in most respects

ITEM	RATING					NO OPPORTUNITY TO OBSERVE
	1	2	3	4		
Knowledge of rules as shown by performance						
Competence in playing his position						
Use of strategy						
Proficiency in ball-handling skills						

Selection of rating scale. The type of scale to be used depends upon the type of information needed. If there is no reason to compute a numerical score, the use of numbers is redundant since each numerical value must be described anyway. There may be occasion when it is necessary to save space or where the description of each category is so involved that it is impractical to include it on the rating form, and clarity may be improved by using numbers or descriptive words.

It may be preferable to combine types of rating forms. Frequently the numerical and graphic types are combined advantageously in situations where a numerical score is desired. For example:

Check the category which best describes your estimate of how the player performs in his particular area of play.

ITEM	0 NEVER	1 SELDOM	2 USUALLY	3 ALWAYS
Competent in covering his zone	——	——	——	——
Makes correct decisions in working with team-mates	——	——	——	——
Knows the plays and fulfills his responsibility in carrying them out	——	——	——	——
Moves easily from defensive to offensive play	——	——	——	——
Shows skill in ball-handling under pressure	——	——	——	——
Is courteous to officials and other players	——	——	——	——

The number of categories to be used depends upon the degree of exactness desired. If only two categories are used, the discrimination would show the extremes such as "very much, very little," "yes, no," or "passed, failed." The varying degrees of behavior between the extremes would be disregarded.

If 100 categories were used, the discrimation from one extreme to the other would be broken down into very minute details ranging from 1 to 100. It is obvious that the construction of such a scale would be a monumental task and an observer's attempts to use such an instrument would be ludicrous. When ten categories are set up many raters fail to use all of them. In general, three to five categories provide adequate data and make it possible for the rater to distinguish accurately between the units on the scale.

Words such as excellent, good, average, poor have little meaning in themselves and should be further defined if they are used. Words and phrases identifying the particular behavior being rated should be used, and they should be specifically defined in the directions to the rater, by describing the particular behaviors to which they refer.

How to Evaluate Movement Skills in Sports, Dance and Aquatics Using Principles of Movement

Since movement is central to living, efficiency in movement is a goal which each individual needs to achieve. An understanding of the mechanics of movement is helpful to the individual in learning new movement patterns or in improving already acquired patterns.

One of the developmental tasks is that of learning to manage a changing body. At puberty, for example, changes in height, in distribution of body weight, in length of extremities will cause changes in the center of gravity, in leverage, with accompanying changes in quality of movement. The middle-aged adult may also find changes occuring in distribution of weight which will affect his movement patterns, as may the aged. At certain growth stages the individual must modify his old movement patterns to meet the demands of a "new" body. This may consist of actually learning new movement patterns.

In evaluating form in the performance of movement skills the values are the laws and principles of the mechanics of movement. These include the laws of stability, Newton's laws of motion and the laws of levers (3, 8).

How to construct a check list to evaluate form.   The preliminary step in the construction of a check list is setting up a work sheet which lists the values and shows the specific application from each value. The applications may then be stated in check list form. In evaluating how a person moves, his "form" in a selected skill, the laws and principles which govern the mechanics of movement for the particular skill are the values.

The following illustration shows the development of a check list from the work sheet. The skill to be evaluated is fielding a baseball.

Work Sheet for Constructing a Check List

Skill to be evaluated: fielding a baseball

VALUES—MECHANICAL PRINCIPLES (3, 8)	APPLICATION
When a body is moving, it will continue to move until stopped by an external force.	Other forces acting on the ball are gravity and wind resistance. Fielder must move into position to catch ball, taking these factors into account.
The more gradually a moving body loses its kinetic energy, the less is the shock of impact.	Slow down the ball as it touches the hands by "giving" with it.
To lessen the force of impact increase the size of the body surface which is receiving the force.	Use both hands to increase size of surface. Use glove.
The body becomes more stable in a given direction if the base of support is widened toward the given direction of movement.	Feet in forward stride position facing ball.

Check List for Evaluating

(fielding a baseball)

Observe the student's performance in each item listed and check those which he performs correctly.

NAMES OF STUDENTS

ITEMS									
Judges flight of ball accurately. Is in position to receive it.									
Traps ball in palms of both hands or uses glove correctly.									
"Gives" with the ball.									
Stance is forward stride toward direction of ball.									

How to construct a rating scale to evaluate form. The initial steps in constructing a rating scale are the same as those for constructing a check list, determination of values and application to the trait being rated. In addition to these procedures is the selection and description of the categories to determine the degree in which the individual being rated possesses the particular skill.

An illustration of how the check list previously described may become a rating scale follows.

Instruction to the Rater:

Descriptions of the categories for rating the student's performance in fielding a baseball are given below.

0—Not executed	None of the trait being rated. No performance.
1—Poorly executed	Performs the trait but very inadequately. Inconsistent in performance. Appears awkward and unsure.
2—Acceptably executed	Performance is what average person of his classification would do. Adequately done so that results are satisfactory.
3—Well executed	Skillful execution. Leaves little to be desired in performance of trait.

Rating Scale

FIELDING A BASEBALL

_____   _____
(Student's name)   (Skill being rated)

Observe the student's performance in each item listed. Check the category which best describes his performance.

ITEMS	0 NOT EXECUTED	1 POORLY EXECUTED	2 ACCEPTABLY EXECUTED	3 WELL EXECUTED
Judges flight of ball accurately. Is in position to receive it.				
Traps ball in palms of both hands.				
"Gives" with ball.				
Feet in forward stride position.				

It is helpful to the raters if a demonstration of each category is given before they rate the students. If they can *see* what is meant by "average" performance and by "skillful" performance, they are all more likely to be using the same criteria in judging the students.

How to Evaluate Movement Skills Using Standards for Performance in the Activity

Standards for skill performance, or activity "objectives" such as accuracy in throwing or skill in catching, are measured by skill tests which assess achievement in specific activity skills. There are tests to measure basket shooting, dribbling, hockey dribble and pass, softball pitching, softball distance throw, volleyball serve, forward pass for distance and many others.

Some of these tests have little value for the physical education teacher in the usual activity situation since they were constructed for the collection of research data to solve other problems and require elaborate equipment, unlimited time and ideal testing conditions which are impractical for use in the public school. Although some tests have been constructed for the express purpose of use in physical education classes, each situation may be unique and may prohibit the use of the test as it is described by the test constructor. If the teacher wishes to change the test in any way, the statistical reliability and validity is immediately open to question and the results have little meaning. When a standardized test is used, the instructions for administering it must be followed exactly.

The assumption is that a standardized test is made for nation-wide use and that the material covered in such a test is subject matter that is "standardized," taught in any classroom or gymnasium in the nation. Since skill tests measure activity skills which are common to most physical education programs in the nation plus the fact that the primary goal of such tests is the activity objective or end result (how many baskets are scored? How many yards is a ball kicked?), the assumption is tenable under these conditions.

It is also assumed, however, that the norms for such tests are computed from a sample of subjects which is representative of all students in every kind of school situation throughout the nation. In using such a test it is important to examine carefully the subjects upon whom the test was standardized. The teacher may find that these subjects differ to a marked degree from the students in his classes and the test would not be suitable for his particular group.

Consequently, many physical education teachers in the field rely on the tests they construct themselves for their own particular situation, frequently with disastrous results because of their own limitations in test construction procedures.

Certainly any teacher can learn how to construct a skill test. The knowledges required for this may be readily obtained by reading the test construction literature and by acquiring elementary statistical understandings, which are degree requirements in numerous teacher education institutions today. Skill in test construction comes with practice in constructing tests and if such practice is not available during the teacher preparation experiences, it may be acquired while on the job.

The values to be achieved in constructing skill tests.   The objective skill test is concerned with the end result and the values are the standards of performance in achieving the end result. How far can the individual throw? How accurate is he in serving the volley ball?

Conditions to be considered in constructing a skill test.   The skill test may be constructed to measure achievement in the particular performance *only*, such as striking a wall target with a volley ball a given number of times within a given time interval, or it may be constructed to measure achievement in the activity in which it is used, such as the game of volley ball. The test should meet the following conditions, whatever its primary purpose: (*a*) it should measure important skills; (*b*) it should be similar to the real situation in which it is used; (*c*) it should allow for the performance of only one person at a time; (*d*) it should have an adequate number of trials; (*e*) it should be economical of time, space and equipment; (*f*) it should have clear and simple directions and accurate scoring procedures; (*g*) it should discriminate among the different abilities being measured.

a) The test should measure important skills. If it is to be used as a measure of achievement in the activity, it must test a skill or skills which are important in the performance of the activity. It is sometimes possible to construct one test which combines several skills such as a dribble and shoot test in basket ball or it may measure only one skill. In selecting skill tests it is important to analyze them carefully according to the skills being measured. A tennis test which measures the tennis serve for distance is of dubious value in measuring achievement in the game of tennis. Rules changes have also occurred since the construction of some of the older tests and they are no longer valid in measuring the sport as it is played today.

b) The test should be similar to the real situation. Skill tests will be better measures of achievement in the particular activity if they are performed in situations similar to their use in the activity. For example, a test of batting ability where the individual bats the ball from a stationary batting tee has little in common with the game of baseball where the batter must strike a moving target. It is conceivable that an individual may do well striking a ball from a batting tee and be incapable of striking a pitched ball successfully.

c) The test should allow for the performance of only one person at a time. It would seem that a very simple way to improve the batting test would be to provide a pitcher who pitched a given number of balls to the batter. This presents another problem, however. Each person being tested must have the same test conditions as every other person being tested in the particular skill, and what pitcher is capable of pitching even two balls that are exactly the same as to speed, position, and spin?

This problem arises in measuring skills used in games which involve more than one person such as volleyball, football, tennis or badminton. The ingenuity of the test constructor is challenged in solving the problem of how to construct a skill test which is like the game and still allows the performance of only one person. Some of the procedures which have been used in an attempt to overcome the difficulty are: (1) stationary objects are used in place of persons to simulate game conditions such as setting up obstacles for the subject to maneuver around; (2) a wall target has been used from which the subject retrieves his own rebounds with the score being the number of times he can kick, volley, bat, throw, strike the particular object into the target in a given period of time; (3) instruments such as a catapult have been constructed to repeat the desired action an infinite number of times.

All of these procedures have disadvantages. There is considerable difference between maneuvering around a stationary bench and a live guard in basketball or a halfback in football. A rebounding object has different characteristics than one which is given impetus by another player, and most schools do not own a catapult.

d) The test should have an adequate number of trials. The higher the degree of accuracy needed for the performance of a given skill the greater the number of trials needed to measure the achievement of the individual. It would be advantageous indeed if each test could be a one-trial test, one throw at the basket, one strike at the baseball, one throw at a target. Unfortunately, the individual is so variable in his ability to perform a skill that his first trial may be perfect and every other trial thereafter complete failures, or vice versa. Skills requiring maximum effort such as a distance throw or speed in swimming need fewer trials to measure the particular achievement. Many of these may be measured in one or two performances if the individual gives all out effort on each performance. The greater the number of trials, the more time it takes to measure one person and the more impractical is the test for use in the school situation where each class may have 50 or 60 students.

e) The test should be economical of time, space and equipment. In addition to economy of time the physical education teacher is confronted with the problems of space and equipment. A test may take only one minute to administer to an individual, but it may also take the entire playing field and expensive or unavailable equipment which makes it impractical for most physical education situations. A distinct advantage of a teacher-constructed test is that it may be tailored to fit the particular situation, the students, the space, the equipment and the program.

f) Directions should be clear and scoring should be precise. Elaborate scoring procedures provide too much opportunity for error and are extremely impractical for the school situation where the teacher must rely on student help in administering and scoring the tests.

g) The test should discriminate among the different abilities being measured. If most scores are massed around zero, the test is too difficult for the particular group and conversely if most of the scores are at the high end of the distribution, the test is too easy. Under either condition the test will not discriminate between the skilled and the unskilled. In selecting a published test the teacher must be sure to choose one that is of suitable difficulty for the group he is testing. A test validated for advanced tennis players is likely to be a poor instrument for measuring achievement of beginning tennis players.

Statistical evaluation of data in constructing a skill test. Conditions to be considered in constructing a skill test include statistical criteria for the evaluation of data. These criteria are (1) test reliability, (2) test validity and (3) test objectivity.

Statistical reliability of a test indicates its consistency or the degree to which it may be relied upon to give the same results from one administration to another. The statistical technique used for computing reliability, validity and objectivity of a test is the correlation technique. Correlation shows the relationship between two measures taken on the same group of individuals and is expressed by a single number called a correlation coefficient. The correlation coefficient may have a value of -1, which indicates a perfect negative relationship, through zero, which shows no relationship, to $+1$, a perfect positive relationship. Thus the correlation coefficient may be any value on a continuum from $-$ to $+1$, but it can never be a value greater than either of these.

It is unusual for perfect negative or positive relationships to result because of errors in measuring, variations in measuring instruments and variability in individuals. If one were to obtain a perfect relationship in computing the reliability of a skill test, he would do well to re-check his data collection procedures and statistical computations for bias or error.

Correlation is a rank order relationship. For example, a test may be administered to a group of students twice in succession under the same testing conditions. The students may score much higher on the second administration of the test due to learning which may have resulted from the practice effect which carried over to the second administration. The *size* of the score does not affect the correlation coefficient. The rank order of the individuals from one administration to the next determines the size of the coefficient. If the rank order stays exactly the same with no exceptions, the result is a perfect positive correlation, even though all subjects may have made higher scores the second time.

Statistical reliability of a skill test is determined by the *test-retest* method or by the *split-half* method.

The test-retest method is most commonly used in determining the reliability of a skill test, that is, the subjects are tested by the same administrator under the same conditions twice. For example, a twenty trial free throw test in basketball is administered to a group of ninth-grade boys and is repeated under exactly the same conditions by the same administrator on the following day. The scores for the first administration of the test are correlated with the scores for the second administration of the test. If a high relationship results, the rank order of the boys stayed the same with few exceptions, and the twenty-trial test is said to be reliable, or consistent, for this group of boys. If this group is representative of ninth-grade boys in the school, the test may be considered reliable for all ninth-grade boys in this school system.

If the correlation coefficient is not satisfactory, the data may be treated in other ways. For example, the score for the *last* ten trials of the first administration may be correlated with the score for the *last* ten trials of the second administration. If a high relationship results, it may be due to the practice effect of the first ten trials which may have resulted in more consistent shooting by each subject on the remaining ten trials. The test would now become a ten-trial test preceded by ten practice trials which are not scored.

One of the hazards of the test-retest method is the difficulty involved in providing the same testing conditions for both administrations of the test. If there is a lapse of several days between the first and second administrations of the test, the testing conditions may be very different: (*a*) some subjects may have practiced the test or may have had experiences which affected their performance, while other subjects may not have had such experiences; (*b*) if the test is administered out of doors, the weather conditions, such as wind or heat, may be different; (*c*) if the test is administered at a different time of day, it may affect performance, for example immediately after lunch or when students are fatigued at the end of the day as compared to early in the morning; (*d*) motivation of the student may be different in that he may be tired, bored, sick or emotionally upset.

Even if the test were administered on two consecutive days, the same problems may exist. If the test were administered twice to the same subjects on the same day the problem of fatigue may enter in particularly on a test requiring strenuous effort, many trials or boring repetitions which affect interest and motivation. The test constructor must be aware of these problems and must plan carefully to minimize them as much as possible.

The split-half method for determining reliability may be used when the test has a large number of trials. The test is administered once and the score for the first half of the trials is correlated with the score for the second half. By applying a statistical formula called the Spearman-Brown formula to the obtained correlation coefficient, it is possible to estimate the size of the correlation coefficient if the test had been administered twice.

For example, the twenty-trial free throw test is administered to the group of ninth-grade boys. The score for the first ten trials is correlated with the score for the remaining ten trials. If the coefficient is acceptable with the rank order of the subjects remaining approximately the same from the first ten trials to the last ten trials, the ten-trial test is reliable. Theoretically, this is using the test-retest method where the first ten trials constitute the first administration of the test and the second ten trials the second administration.

If, however, the correlation coefficient were low, the reliability of a twenty-trial test may be estimated by applying the Spearman-Brown formula to the obtained coefficient.

Another procedure used in the split-half method is the odd-even where the score for the odd-numbered trials is correlated with the score for the even-numbered trials and the Spearman-Brown formula is used to estimate the correlation coefficient for the entire test. An advantage of the odd-even technique is that fatigue factors, practice effects and other changes in conditions are uniformly distributed over the trials in both halves of the test.

In computing the reliability of a skill test at least 50 subjects should be used and frequently test constructors attempt to obtain data on 100 or more subjects. When a small number of subjects is used, chance may operate heavily in determining the results and if the test were administered a third time, the rank order might change noticeably from what it appeared to be after two administrations.

Procedures for computing the correlation coefficient include the Spearman Rank Correlation and the Pearson Product-Moment Correlation. The Spearman Rank Correlation is frequently referred to as the "Spearman Rho." An illustration of this process follows:

SCORES MADE BY SUBJECTS ON GRIP STRENGTH AND DISTANCE RUN

Subject	Grip (pounds)	Run (yards)
A	200	180
B	158	90
C	170	97
D	108	62
E	198	104
F	128	95
G	194	120
H	162	110
I	148	87
J	138	110

1. List the subjects and each subject's scores, placing the subjects in rank order from high to low according to the first set of scores (called the X variable).
2. Indicate the rank of each score for both variables (the X and Y variables).
3. Compute the difference between the two ranks.
4. Square the differences and sum the column.
5. Compute the formula: $r_s = 1 - \dfrac{6(\Sigma D^2)}{N^3 - N}$

   where r_s = RHO

   Σ = summation

   D^2 = rank differences, squared

   N = number of cases

Subject	Variable X (Grip)	Variable Y (Run)	Rank X	Rank Y	D	D^2
A	200	180	1	1	0	0
E	198	104	2	5	3	9
G	194	120	3	2	1	1
C	170	97	4	6	2	4
H	162	110	5	3.5	1.5	2.25
B	158	90	6	8	2	4
I	148	87	7	9	2	4
J	138	110	8	3.5	4.5	20.25
F	128	95	9	7	2	4
D	108	62	10	10	0	0

N = 10

48.50

$$r_s = 1 - \frac{6(48.5)}{1000 - 10} = 1 - \frac{291}{990} = 1 - .293$$

$$r_s = .707$$

Procedures for computing the Pearson Product-Moment correlation coefficient (r) may be found in the statistical references at the end of the chapter (4, 6, 7).

In interpreting the coefficient of correlation, any coefficient which is not zero indicates some relationship between the two measures, either positive or negative. For example, a correlation coefficient computed between two administrations of a skill test with a coefficient resulting in zero would show that there was no relationship between the results of the two administrations. Some of the low scorers on the first administration scored high on the second and some individuals who made high scores on the first administration scored lower than the other subjects on the second administration, with no regular pattern of change.

If such a coefficient resulted in − .92, most of the high scorers on the first administration were low scorers on the second and the low scorers were high scorers with a regular pattern of reversal showing few exceptions. If the correlation coefficent were a perfect negative relationship, −1.00, the rank order would be reversed on the second administration with *no* exceptions.

The greater the distance from zero toward +1.00, the more reliable the test. Test constructors and test users set their own standards for test reliability levels. These are usually around .80 or better for most skill tests.

Low reliability may be due to poor instructions, too few trials, lack of precision in scoring, involvement of more than one performer and lack of motivation on the part of the subjects. Reliability may be improved by alleviating these problems, by increasing the number of subjects and by using a more heterogeneous group with a wider range of abilities.

Statistical validity of a test means the degree to which a test measures what it professes to measure—its truthfulness. To obtain the validity of a skill test, the test scores are correlated with criterion scores.

For example, how valid a measure of basketball playing ability is the basketball wall pass test? To answer this question a criterion or standard for ability in basketball must first be determined. The scores obtained on the basketball wall pass are correlated with the criterion scores. If the correlation results are satisfactory, the test is considered to be valid, that is, performance in the basketball wall pass test would agree with performance in playing basketball as measured by the criterion.

There are three types of criteria which have been used to validate skill tests. These are scores obtained from ratings of qualified judges, scores obtained from the results of tournament standings and scores obtained from other validated tests.

Obtaining criterion scores from judges' ratings is one of the more commonly used methods. The usual procedure is to construct a rating scale, to train the judges in the use of the scale and to provide ample time for the judges to observe the individuals being rated under favorable conditions for performance.

It is assumed that qualified judges using a well-constructed rating scale will estimate accurately the student's achievement in the particular activity. Unfortunately, correlations between judges' ratings tend to be discouragingly low. Practice trials by the raters with a comparison of results improves the consistency between raters. Categories which show lack of agreement by the raters should be revised before the instrument is used in the actual testing. One of the chief errors in rating is that caused by lack of common agreement as to definition of traits being rated.

Whenever possible, it is advisable to use at least three judges, assuming that all are well qualified to rate the particular performance. A composite score is obtained for each subject by totaling, or averaging, the scores of all the judges. Another procedure is to use the midscore rather than the mean.

The results of tournament rankings may be used as a criterion for activities where individual scores are obtained. This presents difficulties in team games where there are no individual scores, only group performance.

Another method is to use the scores obtained from a previously validated test which measures achievement in the particular activity. The criterion for validating the previously validated test was undoubtedly either judges' ratings, tournament standings, another valid test or combinations of all three criteria. Until better criteria are established, the validation of skill tests as measures of achievement in an activity will continue to be a problem.

When a skill test measures *only* performance in the test itself, it is not necessary to validate against an outside criterion. This is called internal or presumptive validity. For example, if presumptive validity were used, the softball throw for distance would purport to measure only achievement in throwing a softball under the particular test conditions for a particular distance. It would *not* claim to measure achievement in the game of softball nor would it profess to be a measure of arm strength, hand-eye coordination or any other factor. If any such claims were made for it, validation against an external criterion would be essential.

When two or more tests are combined to measure achievement in an activity, a test battery is constructed. The following procedures are used to construct a test battery:

1. Compute the reliability of each test item;
2. Compute the validity of each test item;
3. Compute the correlation coefficient between each test and every other test to be considered for the battery;
4. Combine those tests into a battery which have high validity coefficients and low intercorrelations with the other tests in the battery, since tests which correlate high with each other are measuring the same thing;
5. Compute a multiple correlation coefficient for the combined tests to determine the validity of the battery and the weighting of each test in the battery.

For example, a battery of volley ball tests described in the literature (7) consists of a Repeated Volleys Test and a Serve Test. The criterion for validating each of the tests was subjective ratings by four judges. The validity coefficient for the Repeated Volleys Test was .72 and for the Serve Test, .63, with an intercorrelation between the two tests of .39. The low intercorrelation indicates that the tests are measuring different things and will not be wasteful if used together to measure volley ball playing ability. The validity of the combined tests was .81 with the criterion.

Statistical objectivity means the degree to which equally competent administrators obtain the same results from administering the same test to the same subjects. Objectivity of the skill test may be determined by computing the correlation coefficient between the scores obtained by two different administrators testing the same subjects. This may be awkward to obtain because one administrator must test the same subjects twice under the same conditions to determine reliability, and it would be necessary for the second administrator to test the subjects *after* the second administration which entails three administrations of the test. This may cause difficulties because of the amount of time involved and the problem of motivation. A test would have to be very interesting to avoid boredom on the part of the subjects during a third consecutive administration.

An alternate method for obtaining objectivity is to have two scorers working during the first administration of the test. The results obtained by Scorer A are correlated with the results obtained by Scorer B; if the correlation coefficient is acceptable, the test is considered to be objective. Actually when this procedure is used, the coefficient indicates that the test may be scored accurately but there is no way of knowing the objectivity of the instructions and other administrative procedures.

Reliability and validity are always reported by competent test constructors, but objectivity is frequently omitted, undoubtedly because of the problems involved in obtaining it. In such cases it is assumed that standardized directions and accurate scoring will result in objectivity if the test is reliable and valid.

How to administer a skill test. Preliminary arrangements for administering a skill test are:

1. Set up equipment, mark target areas, blow up balls to regulation size, have stop watches ready, prepare testing area and testing materials according to exact specifications as described in the test.

2. Completely familiarize yourself with exact directions for administering the test including instructions to the student, demonstration and scoring. If the test is timed, be sure that timers are competent in the use of the stop watch. It is wise to have several practice administrations of the test before the test period. This may be done by testing students who will serve as assistants before administering the test to the class.

3. If using assistants in any capacity, train them *before* the testing date and give them opportunity to practice on each other.

4. Plan carefully for the organization of the group to be tested. If possible, have several testing stations so that several people may be tested at one time. Decide ahead of time which students will be at which station, how rotation will occur, where they will go when they are finished and what they will do while they are waiting to be tested. Students object strenuously—and rightly so—when testing procedures are inefficient and they are forced to sit in boredom for long periods of time while waiting to be tested.

5. Prepare score cards ahead of time. If students are being tested in groups, a group score card may be used:

Basketball Wall Pass

NAME	TRIAL 1	TRIAL 2	TRIAL 3	TRIAL 4
Adams, George				
Aster, Ellis				
Beers, Shirley				

If it is better to have students moving independently from one station to another, an individual score card may be prepared for each student:

Name_____ Class_____

BASKETBALL WALL PASS
Trial 1   Trial 2   Score

1/2 MINUTE BASKET SHOOTING
Score

DRIBBLE AND SHOOT
Trial 1 _____
Trial 2 _____
Trial 3 _____

Score_____

Free Throw Shooting
Trial 1 _____   Trial 6 _____
Trial 2 _____   Trial 7 _____
Trial 3 _____   Trial 8 _____
Trial 4 _____   Trial 9 _____
Trial 5 _____   Trial 10 _____

Score_____

Fig. 10-1.

The actual administration of the test will be facilitated if one person is assigned to distribute score cards as students enter the testing area and another person is responsible for seeing that students move from station to station at the proper times. General directions should be given to all students at the beginning of the testing period so they understand what is expected of them.

If only one test is being administered using several different stations, the test may be explained and demonstrated to all students before they go to their stations. If several different tests are being administered, each administrator may describe his particular test to each group as it arrives to be tested.

Test administrators and assistants should provide an encouraging and helpful atmosphere for each student being tested. It is very difficult for an individual to do his best when the administrator and observers are critical and derisive. In scoring a test accurately it is essential that the scorer be continually alert. Poorly administered tests result in biased and inaccurate scores and in negative attitudes on the part of the students.

How to interpret test scores. Measures of central tendency and variability are used to compare a given score with other scores in the distribution and are described in Chapter 11. In addition to these measures standard scores or norms are used to compare a score obtained on one test with those obtained on different tests. This is done by expressing all scores in terms of a common denominator.

The term *standard* should not be confused with *standard score.* A standard refers to a described goal which is to be achieved. A standard score is determined from the performance of individuals in a particular group—what these individuals are able to achieve in the particular quality being measured.

Physical education skill tests reported in the literature usually include a set of norms. These norms may have been computed on a limited sample of subjects. For example, a set of standard scores measuring achievement in volley ball was computed from data obtained from 120 high school girls in a mid-western city. These particular girls may not necessarily be representative of high school girls in other parts of the country. If the scores obtained from administering this same volley ball test to a group of high school girls in Long Beach, California are above or below the test norms, it only means that these scores are above or below the scores obtained from the 120 high school girls in the mid-western city. It neither indicates superior or inferior achievement in volley ball nor does it indicate that the norms should be used as standards for performance in volley ball.

It is a misconception among teachers and students that norms published with tests are national norms and should be treated with respect as being the final word on pupil achievement. Because of variations from one school to another in respect to abilities of students, competence of teachers, types of equipment, nature of experiences, length of school terms, it is hardly conceivable that any one set of norms would be suitable for an entire nation.

Under most circumstances it is a better procedure to derive a set of norms within the school itself. This may be done by measuring achievement of students in the school over a two or three year period. Norms computed from these scores will more likely be representative of the particular groups in the particular situation. When the nature of the situation changes, new norms may be established.

As has been stated, standard scores are not the same as standards. The student who scores highest on a particular scale may still be a dub in volley ball when compared to standards for good play in volley ball. Standard scores most frequently used in interpreting skill tests are T-scores and percentiles and are described in Chapter 11.

Tests of achievement in movement skills. There are numerous tests of movement skills in the field which should be revewed by the teacher or leader who is looking for such measures. If there are no suitable tests to measure the particular skill or activity, the teacher or leader should construct a test to serve the purpose.

If a described test is changed in any respect, such as number of trials, length of time, equipment or size of target, the test actually becomes a *new test* and must be evaluated against the test construction criteria including statistical reliability, objectivity and validity.

The tests included in the following recommended list have been selected according to these criteria:

1. Each test is functional for teaching-learning purposes.

2. The facilities and equipment required for administering the test are available in most schools and recreation areas.

3. The test is properly constructed and is reasonably reliable and valid.

Many of these tests have been printed in the *Research Quarterly* of the American Association for Health, Physical Education, and Recreation and are easily accessible to the student through library facilities.

ARCHERY

Hyde, Edith I., "An Achievement Scale in Archery," *Research Quarterly*, Vol. 8, No. 2: 109-116, May, 1937.

BADMINTON

French, Esther and Evelyn Stalter, "A Study of Skill Tests in Badminton for College Women," *Research Quarterly*, Vol. 20, No. 3: 257-272, October, 1949.

Lockhart, Aileen and Frances McPherson, "The Development of a Test of Badminton Playing Ability," *Research Quarterly*, Vol. 20, No. 4: 402-405, December, 1949.

Miller, Frances A., "A Badminton Wall Volley Test," *Research Quarterly*, Vol. 22, No. 2: 208-213, May, 1951.

Scott, M. Gladys, "Achievement Examination in Badminton," *Research Quarterly*, Vol. 12, No. 2: 242-250, May, 1941.

BASEBALL

Hooks, G. Eugene, "Prediction of Baseball Ability through an Analysis of Measures of Strength and Structure," *Research Quarterly*, Vol. 30, No. 1: 38-43, March, 1959.

Kelson, Robert E., "Baseball Classification Plan for Boys," *Research Quarterly*, Vol. 24, No. 3: 304-307, October, 1953.

BASKETBALL

Knox, Robert Dawson, "An Experiment to Determine the Relationship between Performance in Skill Tests and Success in Playing Basketball," in *Measurement in Physical Education* by Donald K. Mathews, Philadelphia: W. B. Saunders Co., 1958, pages 166-169.

Jones, Edith, "A Study of Knowledge and Playing Ability in Basketball for High School Girls," in *Measurement and Evaluation in Physical Education* by M. Gladys Scott and Esther French, Dubuque, Iowa: William C. Brown Company, 1959, pages 158-164.

Scott, M. Gladys, "Passing Test," in *Measurement and Evaluation in Physical Education* by M. Gladys Scott and Esther French, Dubuque, Iowa: William C. Brown Company, 1959, pages 158-164.

BOWLING

Martin, Joan, "Bowling Norms for College Men and Women," *Research Quarterly*, Vol. 31, No. 1: 113-116, March, 1960.

Phillips, Marjorie and Dean Summers, "Bowling Norms and Learning Curves for College Women," *Research Quarterly*, Vol. 21, No. 4: 377-385, December, 1950.

DANCE

Ashton, Dudley, "A Gross Motor Rhythm Test," *Research Quarterly*, Vol. 24, No. 3: 253-260, October, 1953.

DIVING

Bennet, LaVerne Means, "A Test of Diving for Use in Beginning Classes," *Research Quarterly*, Vol. 13, No. 1: 109-115, March, 1942.

FIELD HOCKEY

Schmithals, Margaret and Esther French, "Achievement Tests in Field Hockey for College Women," *Research Quarterly*, Vol. 11, No. 3: 84-92, October, 1940.

FOOTBALL (TOUCH)

Borleske, Stanley E., "A Study of the Achievement of College Men in Touch Football," reported by Frederick W. Cozens in the Ninth Annual Report of the Committee on Curriculum Research of the College Physical Education Association, Report of Subcommittee Four, *Research Quarterly*, Vol. 8, No. 2: 73-78, May, 1937.

GYMNASTICS

Swarig, Leopold F., "Judging and Evaluation of Competitive Apparatus or Gymnastic Exercises," *Journal of Health and Physical Education*, Vol. 6, No. 1: 23-25, 48, 49, January, 1935.

HANDBALL

Cornish, Clayton, "A Study of Measurement of Ability in Handball," *Research Quarterly*, Vol. 20, No. 2: 215-222, May, 1949.

RIDING

Crabtree, Helen Kitner, "An Objective Test for Riding," *Journal of Health and Physical Education*, Vol. 14, No. 8: 419, 446, October, 1943.

SOCCER

McDonald, Lloyd G., "The Construction of a Kicking Skill Test as an Index of General Soccer Ability," in *Measurement in Physical Education* by Donald K. Mathews, Philadelphia: W. B. Saunders Co., 1958, pages 175, 176.

Schaufele, Evelyn F., "The Establishment of Objective Tests for Girls of the Ninth and Tenth Grades to Determine Soccer Ability," in *Measurement and Evaluation in Physical Education* by M. Gladys Scott and Esther French, Dubuque, Iowa: William C. Brown Company, 1959, pages 187-198.

SOFTBALL

Research Committee, Central Association for Physical Education of College Women, "Repeated Throws, Distance Throw, Fielding Test," in *Measurement and Evaluation in Physical Education* by M. Gladys Scott and Esther French, Dubuque, Iowa: William C. Brown Company, 1959, pages 199-206.

SPEEDBALL

Buchanan, Ruth E., "A Study of Achievement Tests in Speedball for High School Girls," in *Measurement and Evaluation in Physical Education* by M. Gladys Scott and Esther French, Dubuque, Iowa: William C. Brown Company, 1959, pages 211-216.

Smith, Gwen, "Speedball Skill Test for College Women," in *Measurement and Evaluation in Physical Education* by M. Gladys Scott and Esther French, Dubuque, Iowa: William C. Brown Company, 1959, pages 211-216.

SWIMMING

Fox, Margaret G., "Swimming Power Test," *Research Quarterly*, Vol. 28, No. 3: 233-237, October, 1957.

Hewitt, Jack E., "Achievement Scale Scores for Wartime Swimming," *Research Quarterly*, Vol. 14, No. 4: 391-396, December, 1943.

TABLE TENNIS

Mott, Jane A. and Aileen Lockhart, "Table Tennis Backboard Test," *Journal of Health and Physical Education*, Vol. 17, No. 9: 550-551, November, 1946.

TENNIS

Broer, Marion R. and Donna Mae Miller, "Achievement Tests for Beginning and Intermediate Tennis," *Research Quarterly*, Vol. 21, No. 3: 303-313, October, 1950.

TRACK AND FIELD

Cozens, Frederick W., "A Fall Decathlon for Track Squads," *Research Quarterly*, Vol. 9, No. 2: 3-14, May, 1938.

VOLLEYBALL

Brady, George F., "Preliminary Investigations of Volleyball Playing Ability," *Research Quarterly*, Vol. 16, No. 1: 14-17, March, 1945.

French, Esther and Bernice Cooper, "Achievement Tests in Volleyball for High School Girls," *Research Quarterly*, Vol. 8, No. 2: 150-157, May, 1937.

Mohr, D. R. and M. J. Haverstick, "Repeated Volley Tests for Women's Volleyball," *Research Quarterly*, Vol. 26, No. 2: 179-184, May, 1955.

Russell, Naomi and Elizabeth Lange, "Achievement Tests in Volleyball for Junior High School Girls," *Research Quarterly*, Vol. 11, No. 4: 33-41, December, 1940.

Selected References

1. American Association for Health, Physical Education, and Recreation, *Research Methods in Health, Physical Education, and Recreation* (edited by M. Gladys Scott). Washington, D. C.: American Association for Health, Physical Education, and Recreation, 1959.

2. Bulletin of the California State Department of Education, *Evaluating Pupil Progress, Vol. XXI, No. 6*. Sacramento: California State Department of Education, 1952.

3. Bunn, John W., *Scientific Principles of Coaching*. Englewood Cliffs, N. J.: Prentice-Hall, Inc., 1955.

4. Guilford, J. P., *Fundamental Statistics in Psychology and Education*, 3rd Ed. New York: McGraw-Hill Book Company, Inc., 1956.

5. Mathews, Donald K., *Measurement in Physical Education*. Philadelphia: W. B. Saunders Company, 1958.

6. Ross, C. C. and Julian C. Stanley, *Measurement in Today's Schools*, 3rd Ed. Englewood Cliffs, N. J.: Prentice-Hall, Inc., 1954.

7. Scott, M. Gladys and Esther French, *Measurement and Evaluation in Physical Education*. Dubuque, Iowa: William C. Brown Company Publishers, 1959.

8. Wells, Katharine F., *Kinesiology*, 2nd Ed. Philadelphia: W. B. Saunders Company, 1955.

11

EVALUATION OF SUBJECT MATTER KNOWLEDGES

EVALUATION COMPETENCIES

To *understand*:

1. *how to evaluate subject matter knowledges*
2. *how to construct and evaluate the essay examination*
3. *how to construct and evaluate the objective examination*
4. *how to administer the written examination*
5. *how to organize and interpret test scores*

EXPERIENCES FOR THE STUDENT

1. *Construct, administer and score an essay examination. Evaluate the examination with the subjects to whom it was administered, using the criteria suggested in this chapter.*
2. *Construct a written objective examination which includes only multiple choice and matching items. Administer and score the examination.*
3. *Evaluate the written objective examination in relation to (a) format, (b) statistical validity, (c) difficulty rating and (d) functioning of responses.*
4. *Interpret the data, using the measures of central tendency, variability and percentiles or standard scores.*

Knowledges about subject matter have been measured as a part of the educational system for many years. Before the nineteenth century oral examinations were used for this purpose, but from about the middle of the nineteenth century to the present written examinations of some nature have been used almost exclusively. Written appraisals may be used to measure rote learning of subject matter, problem solving abilities and depth of understanding in applying knowledges.

How to Evaluate Subject Matter Knowledges in the Professional Fields

The values used in constructing the written examination are the subject matter understandings in the specific course experiences. The development of an outline which includes the understandings or knowledges to be assessed is the first step in constructing the examination. Each item in the outline may be weighted according to its relative importance or significance in the subject matter area. For example:

OUTLINE OF KNOWLEDGE EXAMINATION IN SOFTBALL

Items to Be Measured	Per Cent of Test
1. Rules of play	50
2. Terminology	5
3. Strategy	25
4. Skill analysis	10
5. Safety factors	10
Total	100

In this particular softball unit rules and strategy were emphasized. Knowledge about terminology, skill analysis, and safety were a minor part of this particular course experience. Consequently, knowledges about rules and strategy were included in approximately 75 per cent of the examination since these were most significant for this particular group at this time.

Such an outline helps to prohibit over-emphasis of trivial or relatively unimportant aspects of the subject matter being assessed.

The types of tests used most frequently for evaluating knowledges in the professional fields are (a) essay examinations and (b) objective examinations.

How to Construct and Evaluate the Essay Examination

The essay type question measures the student's ability to organize his thinking about the subject in a logical way and to express his thought clearly and effectively. Communication in written form is important in our culture and students need experiences which provide opportunities for such communication.

In addition to evaluating the student's ability in communication, the essay question is useful in measuring knowledges for which the objective examination is poorly adapted. These knowledges are relationships, comparisons and organization.

Limitations of the essay question. The essay question has limitations which prohibit its use under certain conditions:

1. It may not measure the student's knowledge and information about the subject if he is hampered by poor written communication skills.

2. It may not provide a comprehensive measure of the student's information about the subject since he is restricted to answering the two or three questions which form the examination.

3. It may be difficult to score so that all responses to the same question are measured against the same criterion.

Construction of the essay question. Essay questions may be constructed to measure the utilization of knowledge, or they may be constructed in such a way that they measure rote learning. Questions more likely to measure the utilization of knowledge are the "compare-criticize-evaluate" type in which students must think through and apply information.

Questions which encourage recall of memorized materials begin with such words as "who, what, when, where, list, outline."

For example, in answering the question "List five mechanical principles for giving impetus to an object," the student will have an advantage if he has memorized mechanical principles from his textbook or class notes which no doubt include such a list.

Optional questions should be avoided to ensure all students being measured in the same way. All of the students should respond to *all* of the questions.

Scoring may be improved if an outline of the points to be covered in each question are set up in advance, and if all student responses to each question are evaluated before proceeding to the next question.

Evaluating the essay examination. The essay question is not achieving its purpose if it is measuring knowledges which may be better assessed by an objective type examination. Some of the criteria which may be used to subjectively evaluate the essay examination are:

1. Does the question measure the student's ability to organize material?

2. Does it measure his ability to apply knowledge?

3. Is the question clearly focused on a particular problem or area to be discussed?

4. Is the question precisely stated, avoiding amibiguities?

5. Does the examination include enough questions to cover the student's information about the subject?

6. Are optional questions avoided?

7. Are criteria for scoring each question prepared at the time the examination is constructed?

How to Construct and Evaluate the Objective Examination

The objective examination usually provides a more comprehensive coverage of material than does the essay examination. It is faster and easier to score and eliminates bias on the part of the scorer.

The types of items used in the construction of the objective examination are recall and recognition. Recall type items usually assess memory and recognition type items may be constructed to measure memory or to measure problem solving abilities and the application of information.

The recall type questions commonly used are the *short essay* or *sentence* and variations of the *completion* type question. The most commonly used types of recognition questions include the *alternative response*, the *multiple choice* and the *matching*.

The short essay or sentence type question.   These measure recall of memorized materials. It usually begins with such words as "what, when, where, who, list." It may be difficult to score because a student may combine several possible responses into one response or conversely he may separate one response into several responses. For example:

Question: List three criteria for a good skills test.

Answer of Student X: (*a*) statistical reliability (*b*) statistical validity, (*c*) statistical objectivity.

Answer of Student Y: (*a*) statistical reliability, validity and objectivity (*b*) measures important abilities in a gamelike situation (*c*) provides standardized directions and accurate scoring.

In this situation, Student X separated the statistical criteria into three answers and Student Y combined several criteria into three answers. This, of course, provides a problem for the scorer.

The completion type question. The completion question requires the student to complete a statement by filling in blanks with a correct word or phrase. For example:

The major purpose of recreational programs is to provide for the _____ of individuals.

(Correct answer: *leisure*)

Such items omit a key word or phrase in the sentence. They may be advantageous in measuring ability to recall memorized material if they are carefully constructed. Poorly constructed items may deteriorate into a guessing contest in which the student tries to determine which of several possibilities was in the thoughts of the test constructor when he prepared the statement. If the items are constructed by taking a sentence from a text book and omitting a key word or phrase, the student with the photographic memory has a distinct advantage.

The following points should be considered in the construction of such items:

1. Be sure that the purpose of the test is to measure rote learning.

2. Be sure that each sentence is meaningful and covers important information.

3. Avoid taking sentences directly from the text book.

4. Be sure that there is only one correct response for each blank; otherwise scoring is both difficult and time-consuming.

5. Place only one blank in each statement. This avoids unnecessary confusion for the student and also facilitates scoring since one point may be given for each correct answer and all items are weighted equally. Otherwise, one must decide between giving partial scores to certain blanks or weighting some statements more than others.

6. Avoid giving such grammatical clues as using a verb demanding a plural or singular answer or using "a" or "an" directly in front of a blank.

7. Be sure that statements are precise and clear so the student is able to make meaning out of them.

8. Omit only the key word or phrase; when insignificant words or phrases are omitted, the response is either obvious or it is impossible to determine.

9. Be sure that blanks are of uniform length to avoid giving clues as to the length of response expected.

Under most circumstances the recall question would have limited use in health education, physical education and recreation since it is usually preferable to measure the student's ability to utilize rather than to memorize such materials.

If the recall question is used, the short essay is usually superior to the completion type, chiefly because of the difficulty in constructing a completion item which avoids placing the student in the position of trying to out-guess the test constructor.

The alternative response type item. The alternative response item measures the student's ability to recognize correct information as he does the multiple choice and matching type question. The alternative response provides two possible choices of which one is correct. It is familiar to most students as the "true-false" or "right-wrong" type of item, for example:

True   False   1. Strenuous activity is beneficial to individuals
                  of all ages.
                  (Correct answer: *False*)

There are numerous forms for constructing such items. Some of the more familiar are:

Write T for true or F for false on the blank space in front of the statement.

F   1. Strenuous activity is beneficial to individuals of all ages.

Place a plus sign (+) for true and a minus sign (−) for false on the blank in front of the statement.

−   1. Strenuous activity is beneficial to individuals of all ages.

Circle the correct response to the statement.

T   Ⓕ   1. Strenuous activity is beneficial to individuals of all
           ages.

The circling procedure is probably preferable since it is usually clear to the scorer and is readily understood by the student.

Teachers frequently construct alternative response items by taking sentences from the text book and changing approximately half of them to false statements. Although it is easy to cover a vast amount of material this way, the items actually measure the student's ability to recognize text book material and do not discriminate between the student with little understanding and the student with much understanding of the material.

Another disadvantage of this type of item is the opportunity for 50-50 guessing odds. When the results are corrected for guessing, many minus scores may occur which may be very discouraging to the student.

If the test is not corrected *with* the student, which occurs more often than not when it is used as a final examination for grading, the student may leave with misinformation which he tends to accept as true.

If there is a large amount of material to cover and little time available for constructing the examination, the emergency may warrant the use of the alternative response item. The teacher must recognize, however, that the test tends to measure rote learning rather than utilization of knowledge.

If it is advisable to use the alternative response, the following points should be considered in constructing the items:

1. Be sure that the statement is definitely right or wrong, not ambiguous or unclear.

2. Avoid the use of qualifying words such as "small, few, many" since these tend to be ambiguous and obscure the meaning.

3. Avoid using long, involved sentences which may confuse the student and accomplish nothing in measuring his understanding of the subject matter.

4. The score should be corrected for guessing. This is usually done by subtracting the total errors from the total correct answers. For example:

Total number of items in test	= 50
Correct answers	= 32
Incorrect answers	= 4
Omissions	= 14
SCORE (corrected)	= 28

Another procedure for computing the score is the total number of items minus the omissions minus twice the number wrong:

$$50 - 14 - 8 = 28.$$

5. State in the test directions to the student that he will be penalized for guessing.

Frequent use of alternative response tests encourages rote learning which limits their value in health education, physical education and recreation where the emphasis is usually on the student's ability to use information.

The multiple choice type item. The multiple choice item is a statement or question followed by three or more responses from which to choose. This type item may be constructed to measure the student's ability to recognize memorized material or it may be constructed to measure the student's ability to apply facts in the solution of problems.

Opportunities for guessing are not as great as in the alternative response since each question has from three to five choices from which to select the correct answer. Correction for guessing may be used if so desired, applying the same basic formula of correct minus incorrect responses. If there are three choices, the score would be the number of correct responses minus one-half the incorrect responses; if four choices, the score is correct responses minus one-third the incorrect responses, and for five choices, correct minus one-fourth the incorrect.

Some test constructors recommend correcting for guessing and others state that one advantage of the multiple choice test is that it does not require correction for guessing. If most students answer most of the questions, it is not necessary to correct for guessing and the score is the number of correct answers.

One of the disadvantages of the multiple choice type test is the time it takes to construct each item. Questions must be clear and choices plausible with differentiation between choices supported by evidence available to the student. This type of item when poorly constructed may be as ambiguous as a poorly-constructed true-false statement and the selection of the correct response may be as great a guessing contest for the student as the completion items frequently are. On the other hand, an item that includes all possible information may provide clues which suggest the correct answer to every student no matter what his understanding of the subject matter.

If the multiple choice item is constructed for the purpose of measuring the student's understanding and ability to *apply* factual material, the factual material should be made available to him either by an "open book" examination in which the student uses his own materials (text books or class notes) or by including such factual material in the examination. This may be done through the question itself or by supplementary materials such as a separate sheet of rules or formulas.

Points to be considered in constructing multiple choice items are:

1. The preliminary material may be in the form of a direct question or an incomplete statement. The direct question is preferable because

it is less confusing to the student and there are fewer opportunities for grammatical clues than in the incomplete statement. If the incomplete statement is used, it should itself by meaningful.

Example of the direct question:

_____ 1. What is one of the most effective arguments against placing recreation under a state planning board?

    a. Planning board suggests public welfare which implies that recreation is only for the underprivileged who must seek relief.

    b. Planning boards deal only with the conservation aspects of recreation.

    c. Any one board is not competent to deal intelligently with the variety of problems involved in recreation.

    (Best answer: c)

Example of the incomplete statement:

_____ 1. One of the most effective arguments against placing recreation under a state planning board is that

    a. the term, "planning board," suggests public welfare which implies that recreation is only for the underprivileged.

    b. planning boards deal only with the conservation aspects of recreation.

    c. any one board is not competent to deal intelligently with the variety of problems involved in recreation.

    (Best answer: c)

2. There should be from three to five responses, one of which is the "correct" answer or one of which is the "best" answer. The directions to the student should state whether the items are constructed so that only one response is correct and the others definitely incorrect, or if all responses are correct to some degree with one being more correct than the others, the "best" answer.

3. Each distracting response should be credible and related to the idea. Completely unrelated responses serve no purpose since they do not distract anyone. Such a response is non-functioning and should be replaced with a more plausible response.

4. The placement of the correct response in the series should be varied.

5. Avoid setting up a pattern of correct responses.

6. The length of the distractors should be approximately the same as that of the correct response. Otherwise students may soon discover that the correct answer is consistently longer or shorter than the distracting responses.

7. A negative item is one in which the answer is the *incorrect* response with all other responses correct. The negative word in the question should be underlined, for example: Which is <u>not</u> a function of recreational programs?

8. If there are several negative items, it is preferable that they all be grouped together under specific instructions indicating that they are negative.

If the multiple choice item is constructed properly, it may test for depth of understanding and for problem solving abilities. A type of multiple choice is a situation-action question in which a situation is described and several possible solutions are given, one of which is the best solution. This type of question is useful in assessing an individual's understandings of strategy and rules in a sport or game. In addition to the solutions, reasons may be given from which the individual selects those which substantiate the solution he has selected. For example:

Read the following description of a situation in baseball. Check the one action which you believe to be best. Then check the reason or reasons which substantiate the action you have selected.

The situation:

George's team is in the field and he is playing first base position. There are two outs and the right-handed batter who is a poor hitter has three balls and two strikes against him. Two runners are on bases, one runner on first and one on third. The base runner on first base is a slow runner. The score is 6-2 in favor of George's team, and it is the last half of the ninth inning.

Actions:

_____1. George should play a few feet in back of first base.

_____2. George should play approximately 15 yards from first base between first and second base.

_____3. George should play between first and second base but only about 5 yards from first base.

_____4. It makes no difference where he plays as long as he covers first base.

(Best answer: 3)

Reasons:

_____1. If the hitter is extremely fast, he might lay down a bunt even on the third strike and beat it out to first base if the base is not closely covered.

_____2. With two outs it is better to play for the third out and ignore the base runner.

_____3. It would be important to make an effort to pick off the runner on first base if he has been taking a long lead.

_____4. In playing percentages with a poor hitter he will either strike out, hit a ground ball or pop up.

_____5. If the batter normally pulls his hits to the left side, it might be safer to play for a ground ball put-out at second base.

(*Correct reasons are numbers 2 and 4.*)

The matching type item. The matching item may be considered to be a type of multiple choice which measures the student's ability to *recognize* "who, what, where, when" kinds of information.

The format of the matching test includes two columns, one consisting of a list of items and the other consisting of a list of matching words or phrases. The matching column consists of two more responses than the number of items in the first column to prevent the student from using the process of elimination in selecting the final items. For example:

DIRECTIONS: Match the definitions in Column 2 with the terms in Column 1. Each definition may be used only once, and there are two definitions which do not match any of the terms in the list.

Column 1	*Column 2*
_____1. isotonic contraction	a. steady, prolonged contraction
_____2. isometric contraction	b. small, irregular contractions
_____3. tetanus	c. diminished capacity for response
_____4. muscle twitch	d. performance of work
_____5. fatigue	e. muscular effort with no work performed
	f. shortening of the muscle
	g. single contraction and relaxation

(Answers: 1, *d*; 2, *e*; 3, *a*; 4, *g*; 5, *c*)

In constructing matching items, the following points should be considered:

1. There should be two more responses than the number of items.

2. Similar materials should be grouped together in each list of items. For example, muscle physiology, baseball rules and dance terminology should not be mixed together in one list, but should be separated into three homogeneous lists.

3. Lists should include five to ten items. If there are fewer than five items, the process of elimination may give the student an advantage in guessing and if there are more than ten, the list becomes confusing because of length. The matching items should be on the same page with the list of items they answer.

Matching items tend to measure rote learning rather than problem solving abilities.

Some of the games or sports and dance materials may be clarified by using illustrative materials, for example:

_____1. Which step pattern best describes a walk?

     a. — — —   — — —   — — —   — — —

     b. — — — —   — — — — —   — — — —   — — — —

     c. — —   — —   — —   — —

     d. — — — —   — — —   — — —   — — —

     (Answer: *c*)

Diagrams of playing fields, of ball flight and the like may be used advantageously in constructing knowledge tests in certain physical education subject matter areas.

Evaluating the objective examination. The written examination should fulfill the described purpose; it should have an effective format; and it should be statistically acceptable.

If the purpose of the examination is to appraise the student's understanding of the subject matter knowledges and his ability to apply them, the test should be comprehensive enough to cover all important understandings, and the items should be constructed to measure application of knowledge rather than rote memory.

The preliminary outline should be checked to determine what per cent of the test items actually appraise the significant materials in the particular experience. If this is not done, the major portion of the test may actually deal with trivia or stress only one aspect of the experience, particularly if some of the material lends itself more readily to construction of test items.

The format should add to the effectiveness and clarity of the examination and should include the following considerations:

1. The title of the examination, a space for the student's name, score and any other necessary information should be at the top of the first page and should be followed by a statement of the purpose of the examination. The student should understand why he is taking the examination and the use to be made of the results. For example:

Evaluation Procedures
Final Examination, April, 1961

Student's Name_____   Score_____

PURPOSE OF EXAMINATION:

1. To determine the student's knowledge in the construction and evaluation of skill tests, of elementary statistical procedures and of knowledge examinations and his ability to appy such knowledges to the solution of problems.
2. To serve as one basis for appraisal of instruction in the course.
3. To serve as one criterion for determining the course grade.

2. Directions to the student should follow the purpose of the examination. These should be clear and concise and should help him achieve his best in writing the examination. If a time limit is imposed, it should be so stated. If penalties for guessing are used in the scoring, this should be described. It is unnecessary to include such directions as "Do not cheat" and "Keep your eyes on your own paper." Such directions are insulting and annoying to a student and are not conducive to helping him do his best.

3. Test items of the same type should be together in the examination with a set of directions immediately preceding them. Sample questions should be included if the type of item is unfamiliar to the student.

4. It is particularly essential that short essay items have careful instructions, if they are to be evaluated against certain criteria. For

example, if part of the evaluation is on grammar or spelling, this should be indicated.

5. A complete question should be on one page. Split questions are confusing and time-consuming for the student. In the case of multiple choice or matching items this is particularly true; therefore, all responses should be on the same page with the question.

6. It is permissible for the objective examination to include more than one type of item. Some test constructors suggest that a variety of items are more interesting to the student and encourage using several types particularly in long tests. Others recommend using only one type, or at the most two types, indicating that a variety of different types is only confusing, requires more space for different sets of instructions and serves no particular function in appraising the student's knowledge.

If the stated purpose of the examination may be better met by using several types of questions or if one kind of material lends itself better to a particular type of item, it would be logical to construct the types of items which are most functional for the particular purpose. On the other hand, if one particular type of item meets the purpose of the examination better than other types, there is certainly nothing to be gained by forcing the material into many different types of items simply to entertain the student. The types of items to be used, therefore, would depend upon the purpose of the examination and the nature of the material which is being appraised.

7. Items should be placed in order of difficulty from the least to the most difficult. This is encouraging to the student, which is in itself more motivating, and makes it possible for the weaker student to indicate the knowledges he has. Otherwise, if the difficult questions are first, the weak student may never get to those questions he is able to answer.

It is difficult, if not impossible, to use statistical tools to evaluate the essay type question, but the objective type examination may be evaluated in terms of statistical reliability, validity, level of difficulty and for multiple choice items functioning of responses.

Statistical reliability is determined by computing the relationship between (a) two different forms of the test, (b) two administrations of the same form or (c) the odd-numbered items and the even-numbered items in the test.

Reliability of the written objective examination is considered to be of dubious value since it is possible to have a high relationship between the odd-numbered and even-numbered items, or between two different forms of the test or two administrations of the same test, and the test itself may be worthless. A high relationship between the odd-numbered and even-numbered items indicates that the items have been equally distributed according to difficulty. If such a relationship is low, it may easily be improved by placing the items in different order in the test so that half of the difficult items are odd-numbered and half of them are even numbered. In general, it may be assumed that a test which is valid is also reliable, particularly if it includes a large number of items.

Statistical validity is more significant than reliability in the construction of the written objective examination. The validity of the examinaton depends upon the validity of each item in the examination. An item is valid to the extent that it differentiates between the high and low achievers with the validity becoming increasingly greater as more high achievers succeed and more low achievers fail to give the correct response to the item. Validity means how well the test measures what it claims to measure—how well it discriminates between those who have knowledge about the subject and those who do not have knowledge about the subject.

Validity of an item is computed by determining the per cent of high achievers who give the correct response as compared to the per cent of low achievers who give the correct response. Items in which the high group exceeds the low group in correct responses are valid. If both groups are the same, the item does not discriminate and is useless, and if the low group exceeds the high group in correct responses, the item is discriminating against those who have the most information.

Validity of the item may be measured by an "index of discrimination." The Flanagan technique is one of the more simple and useful methods for computing the index of discrimination (4, 7). Briefly, this method follows these procedures:

1. The upper 27% and the lower 27% of the group who took the test are selected for analysis. The upper 27% are labeled the "high" group and the lower 27% are the "low" group.

2. The percentage of "highs" who answered the item correctly are computed and the percentage of "lows" who answered correctly are computed.

3. The percentages are translated into one quantitative figure by using the Flanagan table of indices of discrimination.[1] The higher the index the more valid the item. That is, as more of the highs and fewer of the lows answer the item correctly the more valid is the item.

[1] M. Gladys Scott and Esther French, *Measurement and Evaluation in Physical Education* (Dubuque, Iowa: William C. Brown Company, Publishers, 1959), p. 131.

The *difficulty rating* of the item may be determined by computing the per cent of people who selected the correct answer. This is obtained by dividing the number who selected the correct answer by the total number who took the test. The lower the per cent the more difficult the item. Items which are so difficult that no one answers them correctly or which are so easy that everyone answers them correctly do not discriminate and are useless as far as the validity of the test is concerned. Items of less than 16% or more than 84% difficulty should be dropped.[2]

Functioning of responses should also be analyzed for multiple choice type items. Each response should be selected by at least one person taking the test or it is not functioning and has no use in the test. If a multiple choice item has three possible responses and one does not function, the item has become in reality an alternative response item with two choices.

The test user must decide upon a percentage minimum for a cut-off point on the functioning of responses. Usually if 3 to 5 per cent of those taking the test do not select the response, it is revised or replaced.

How to Administer the Written Examination

The test should be administered under conditions which make it possible for the student to do his best. The physical conditions should be appropriate with good lighting and ventilation, comfortable seating, good writing surfaces and a quiet classroom free from distractions.

Directions and instructions to the student should be written in the test. If there are specific points which may be troublesome or unfamiliar to the student, these should be clarified by the test administrator *before* the students begin to work. The mechanics should be described at this time—the length of time allotted, procedure to be followed when the test is completed.

Students should be discouraged from asking questions during the test since this is distracting to the other students and may also give an unfair advantage unless the test administrator interrupts the class and explains the question and answer to all students.

Tests administered to more than one group of students should have standardized directions which are followed exactly, if the scores are to be compared.

[2] C. C. Ross and Julian C. Stanley, *Measurement in Today's Schools, 3rd Ed.* (Englewood Cliffs, N.J.; Prentice-Hall, Inc., 1954), p. 119.

How to Interpret Test Scores

When the test has been administered and scored, the obtained score may be thought of as a "raw score." An individual score by itself has little meaning and must be interpreted in relation to something. If a predetermined standard has been set, the raw score may be interpreted according to how close it is to meeting the standard.

For example, on a 50 item test where each correct item scored one point, a student received a raw score of 25. If the standard for excellence on this test were achieving the score of 50, this student fell below the standard.

An individual score is usually interpreted by comparing it with scores obtained by other individuals who took the test. For example, 40 students took the 50 item test and the lowest score was 2 and the highest score was 25. Thus, the student who received the score of 25 ranked highest in this particular group, even though he missed half of the items in the test.

If the middle score were known, it would be possible to further interpret a given score by determining whether it were in the upper or lower half of the distribution, on either end of the distribution or in the middle. Measures which determine the middle, average or typical score are called "measures of central tendency." Those most commonly used are the mean, median and mode.

By subdividing the halves of the distribution, it is possible to obtain even greater precision in interpreting an individual score. Measures which show the spread of scores above and below the middle are called "measures of variability" and include the standard deviation, the quartile deviation and the range.

Measures of central tendency. The mean is the arithmetical average and is obtained by summing the scores and dividing by the number who took the test. The formula for computing mean from raw scores is

$$M = \frac{\Sigma X}{N}$$

where M is the symbol for mean, Σ is summation, X is an individual raw score and N is the total number of scores. For example:

Student	Raw Score on Test
M	22
J	29
K	18
A	13
F	25
L	8
D	15
C	18
G	24
S	18

$$\Sigma = 190$$

$$M = \frac{190}{10} = 19$$

In this particular distribution students who made a score higher than 19 are above the mean and those with scores lower than 19 are below the mean.

The median is the middle score which divides the distribution into halves. It may be computed by placing the scores in rank order according to magnitude and counting from either end to the middle score. Theoretically, when the total number of students taking the test is an even number, there is no middle score. In such a situation it is acceptable to average the two middle scores to determine the median. For example:

Student	Raw Score on Test
J	29
F	25
G	24
M	22
K	18
C	18
S	18
D	15
A	13
L	8

$$\frac{N}{2} = \frac{10}{2} = 5 \qquad Mdn = 18$$

In the example the fifth score from the top is 18 as is the fifth score from the bottom. If these two scores were different from each other, the median would be the average of the two scores. In this instance the two scores are the same and the median, or middle score, is 18. If N were an odd number, the score in the middle of the distribution would be the median.

The mode is the score which occurs with the greatest frequency and is obtained by inspection. In the two previous examples the score of 18 occurred more often than did the other scores and is the mode of this particular distribution.

When a distribution is "skewed" with a large number of the scores grouped at either end, the median is the best estimate of the typical score. If the distribution is such that most of the scores are grouped in the middle, the mean is usually used as the measure of central tendency. The mode is seldom used in the treatment of data obtained from tests and may be considered no further.

Measures of variability. The standard deviation shows the spread of scores from the mean and is obtained by summing the squared differences between each individual score and the mean, dividing this sum by the total number who took the test and extracting the square root. Using the same distribution which was used in computing the mean ($M = 19$) for computing the standard deviation:

STUDENT	X (Raw Score on Test)	x (X − M)	x^2
M	22	3	9
J	29	10	100
K	18	− 1	1
A	13	− 6	36
F	25	6	36
L	8	− 11	121
D	15	− 4	16
C	18	− 1	1
G	24	5	25
S	18	− 1	1
			$\Sigma = 346$

$$SD = \sqrt{\frac{346}{10}} = 5.88$$

The formula for computing the standard deviation from raw score is

$$\text{SD} = \sqrt{\frac{\Sigma x^2}{N}}$$

where SD is the symbol for standard deviation, Σ is summation, x is the difference between the individual score and the mean, and N is the total number of scores.

Theoretically, if the distribution is normal, approximately 68 per cent of the scores would fall between one standard deviation below and above the mean. Approximately 13 per cent of the scores would fall between one and two standard deviations above the mean with 13 per cent between one and two standard deviations below the mean. Two to three standard deviations above the mean would include approximately 3 per cent of the scores with the remaining 3 per cent two to three standard deviations below the mean.

In the distribution where the mean is 19 and the standard deviation is 5.88, student F with a score of 25 is better than one standard deviation above the mean, and student J with a score of 29 is almost two standard deviations above the mean.

When letter grades are based on this type of distribution, 68 per cent of the students would receive a "C," 13 per cent a "B" and 13 per cent a "D," with 3 per cent "A" and 3 per cent "F."

Distributions, however, are rarely normal according to this definition and arbitrarily following such a procedure will distort the true picture. If the number of subjects is small or the distribution is skewed, the median and the quartile should be used.

The quartile divides the distribution into fourths. The second quartile, Q_2, is the median, the point in the distribution which divides it in half. The first quartile, Q_1, is the point at which the lower half is equally divided and the third quartile, Q_3, is the point which equally divides the upper half. There is no fourth quartile and there is no zero quartile. If a student scores below Q_1, he is in the lower fourth of the distribution and if he scores above Q_3 he is in the upper fourth.

In the illustration used for computing median (Mdn = 18),

$$Q_3 = 24 \text{ and } Q_1 = 15.$$

The formula for quartile deviation is

$$Q = \frac{Q_3 - Q_1}{2}$$

which would be

$$Q = \frac{24 - 15}{2} = 4.5$$

for this particular distribution.

The range is a rough measure of variability and is obtained by computing the difference between the high and low scores in the distribution. The range is similar to the mode in that neither are highly descriptive of test data and are seldom used.

Procedures for computing mean and standard deviation are relatively simple when the number of cases is small. When there are large numbers, the grouped frequency distribution is used. Scores are grouped in classes according to size. The grouped frequency distribution is made by (a) determining the size of the classes, (b) determining the limits of each class and (c) tabulating each score in its appropriate class. An illustration of this process follows:

SCORES MADE BY FIFTY SIXTH GRADE BOYS
ON THE BASKETBALL WALL PASS TEST

21	20	9	16	13
13	21	17	26	17
19	15	16	17	6
20	16	34	20	16
25	14	28	13	15
18	16	19	13	17
20	18	25	17	20
16	11	17	10	16
14	8	30	30	20
8	25	17	14	22

1. Determine the size of the classes.
   a. Determine the range which is the difference between the lowest and highest scores:

$$
\begin{aligned}
\text{Highest score} &= 34 \\
\text{Lowest score} &= \underline{6} \\
\text{Range} &= 28
\end{aligned}
$$

   b. Divide the range by 15. It is usually advisable to have no more than 20 classes and no less than 12, with 15 classes (more or less) providing a workable distribution:

$$
\begin{aligned}
\text{Range} &= 28 \\
28 \div 15 &= 1.86 + \text{(class size)}
\end{aligned}
$$

   For ease in handling data, the size of the class interval is a whole number. For this particular distribution, therefore, the class interval size would be 2.0.

   Class intervals with whole-numbered mid-points are easier to work with than fractional numbers. Whenever possible, interval sizes of odd numbers (3, 5, 7) are more practical than even-numbered intervals (2, 4, 6). In this particular example, however, if we used an interval size of 1 (an odd number) the mid-point would be a fraction, and there would be 28 classes which are too many for convenience in computation. If the interval size were 3, there would be too few classes, and the resulting computations would be very rough estimates.

2. Determine the limits of each class.
   a. There must be enough classes to include both the lowest and highest scores. A simple way to determine the class limit is to have the lower limit of each class be a multiple of the class interval size. The lowest class must include the lowest score. In this particular distribution the lowest score is 6 which *is* a multiple of the class size, 2. Thus, the lowest class will be 6-7 with a mid-point of 6.5. The highest score, 34, also happens to be a multiple of the class size. The highest class, therefore, is 34-35 with a mid-point of 34.5.

   If, for example, we had a distribution where the lowest score was 16 and the highest score 94, the class interval size would be 5. The lowest class limits would be 15-19 with a mid-point of 17 and the highest class limits would be 90-94 with a mid-point of 92.

b. In the frequency distribution each score loses its own identity and assumes the identity of the mid-point of the class in which it is grouped. For example, there are 14 scores included in the class 16-17 (see frequency distribution which follows). These scores are no longer identified as score 16 or score 17, but all are now considered to be score 16.5, the mid-point of the class. This is significant because it results in what is called a "grouping error." When the mean is computed from the frequency distribution, it is possible that it may result in a different figure than that obtained when the scores are totaled and divided by the number. The larger the class interval size, the greater the opportunity for a large grouping error.

3. Tabulate each score in its appropriate class.

a. The first score recorded in this particular distribution is 21. A "tally" is made under the tabulation column in the class 20-21. Score 13 which is recorded next is tallied in its class, 12-13. All other scores are tallied in their appropriate classes.

b. After all scores are tallied, the number of scores in each class is recorded under the frequency column.

Frequency Distribution of Scores Made by 50
Sixth Grade Boys on the Basketball Wall Pass

Classes	Tabulation	Frequency(f)
34 – 35	/	1
32 – 33		0
30 – 31	//	2
28 – 29	/	1
26 – 27	/	1
24 – 25	///	3
22 – 23	/	1
20 – 21	ЖΖ ///	8
18 – 19	////	4
16 – 17	ЖΖ ЖΖ ////	14
14 – 15	ЖΖ	5
12 – 13	////	4
10 – 11	//	2
8 – 9	///	3
6 – 7	/	1

$$\Sigma = 50$$

The procedure for computing the mean from the grouped frequency distribution is (1) assume a mean, (2) lay off the deviation of each class from the assumed mean. (3) multiply the number of frequencies in each class by is deviation and total the column by adding algebraically, (4) divide the total by the number of cases and multiply by the class interval size, and (5) add to the assumed mean. Thus, the formula for obtaining mean from the grouped frequency distribution is:

$$M = A.M. + \left(\frac{\Sigma fd}{N}\right)i$$

where M is mean
Σ is summation
A.M. is assumed mean
f   is frequency
d   is deviation
N is number of cases
i   is class interval size

To illustrate:

Classes	Tab.	f	d	fd	Computation
34 – 35	/	1	8	8	A. M. = 18.5
32 – 33		0	7	0	
30 – 31	//	2	6	12	Σ fd = –17
28 – 29	/	1	5	5	
26 – 27	/	1	4	4	$\frac{-17}{50}$ = – .34
24 – 25	///	3	3	9	
22 – 23	/	1	2	2	
20 – 21	ЖЖ ///	8	1	8	–. 34 × 2 = –. 68
18 – 19	////	4			18. 5 + –. 68 = 17. 82 (Mean = 17. 82)
16 – 17	ЖЖ ЖЖ ////	14	–1	–14	
14 – 15	ЖЖ	5	–2	–10	
12 – 13	////	4	–3	–12	
10 – 11	//	2	–4	– 8	
8 – 9	///	3	–5	–15	
6 – 7	/	1	–6	– 6	

$$\Sigma = -17$$

1. Assume a mean.
   a. Select any class. The assumed mean is the mid-point of the class. Thus, the class 18-19 was selected and the mid-point, 18.5 was the assumed mean.
   b. Choosing a class nearer the middle of the distribution facilitates computation, although *any* class may be selected.
2. Lay off the deviation of each class from the assumed mean.
   a. The first class above the assumed mean, 20−21, is +1 deviation from the mean. The next class, 22-23, is +2 deviations, and so on. These deviations are placed in the column designated by "d."
   b. The first class below the assumed mean, 16−17 is −1 deviation from the mean. The next class, 14-15, is −2 deviations, and so on. The class which contains the assumed mean is of course, zero deviations from the mean.
3. Multiply the number of frequencies in each class by its deviation and total the column by adding algebraically.
   a. There is 1 frequency in the top class and it deviates 8 classes from the assumed mean. The product of 1 times 8 is 8. This is recorded in the frequency times deviation (fd) column. It may be observed that all products below the mean are negative numbers.
   b. Total the column by adding algebraically. The sum of the positive numbers = 48 and the sum of the negative numbers = −65, with a total of −17.
4. Divide the total by the number of cases and multiply by the class interval size.
   a. The total, −17, is divided by the number of cases, 50, which equals −.34.
   b. The size of the class interval is 2, which multiplied by −.34 equals −.68. This is frequently called the "correction" and is indicated by the formula: $c = \dfrac{i(\Sigma fd)}{N}$
5. Add to assumed mean.
   a. The assumed mean was 18.5 and −.68 added to this results in 17.82. The mean of this distribution as computed from the frequency distribution is 17.82.
   b. When the scores are totaled and divided by N (50), the resulting mean is 17.76, a difference of .06. Although such discrepancies occur between the two methods of computing

mean, due to grouping error as previously stated, the difference is so negligible as to be unimportant.

After computing the mean from the grouped frequency distribution it is relatively simple to compute the standard deviation. This is done by adding another column to the distribution, fd^2, and using the formula:

$$SD = \sqrt{\frac{\Sigma fd^2}{N} - \left(\frac{\Sigma fd}{N}\right)^2} \times i$$

where SD is standard deviation
   Σ is summation
   fd^2 is frequency $\times$ deviation $\times$ deviation
   $(fd)^2$ is frequency $\times$ deviation, quantity squared
   N is number of cases
   i is class interval size

To illustrate, using the same distribution as for computing mean:

Classes	f	d	fd	fd²	Computation
34-35	1	8	8	64	$\frac{\Sigma fd}{N} = -.34$
32-33	0	7	0	0	
30-31	2	6	12	72	$(-.34)^2 = .12$
28-29	1	5	5	25	
26-27	1	4	4	16	$\frac{\Sigma fd^2}{N} = \frac{429}{50} = 8.58$
24-25	3	3	9	27	
22-23	1	2	2	4	
20-21	8	1	8	8	$SD = \sqrt{\frac{\Sigma fd^2}{N} - \left(\frac{\Sigma fd}{N}\right)^2} \times i$
18-19	4				$SD = (\sqrt{8.58 - .12})\,2 =$
16-17	14	−1	−14	14	$2.9 \times 2 = 5.8$
14-15	5	−2	−10	20	
12-13	4	−3	−12	36	$SD = 5.8$
10-11	2	−4	− 8	32	
8-9	3	−5	−15	75	
6-7	1	−6	− 6	36	
				$\Sigma = 429$	

1. Compute fd^2 column; sum the column.
   a. This column is frequency times deviation times deviation. In the fd column we have already computed frequency times

deviation. If we therefore multiply the fd column by the d column, we obtain fd².

b. Total the fd² column, observing that all numbers are now positive as a result of the squaring process.

2. Apply the formula.

a. We have previously obtained $\frac{\Sigma fd}{N}$ in computing the mean, which resulted in −.34. Note that this figure is multiplied by the class interval size in obtaining mean, but is *not* multiplied by the size in obtaining standard deviation.

b. When we square −.34 we obtain .12. Thus,

$$\left(\frac{\Sigma fd}{N}\right)^2 = .12.$$

c. The fd² column is summed and divided by the number of cases. In this distribution, $\frac{429}{50} = 8.58$. The next step in applying the formula is to subtract .12 from 8.58 and extract the square root. The final step in computing standard deviation is to multiply by the class interval size.

The median is found by (1) obtaining 50% of N, (2) count up (or down) the frequency column, (3) compute the correction and (4) obtain the median. To illustrate, using the same frequency distribution:

Classes	f	Computation
34-35	1	50% of N (50) = 25
32-33	0	
30-31	2	Approximated median = 15.5
28-29	1	25 − 15 = 10
26-27	1	
24-25	3	$\frac{10}{14} \times 2 = 1.43$ (correction)
22-23	1	
20-21	8	
18-19	4	
16-17	14	Median = 15.5 + 1.4 = 16.93
14-15	5	
12-13	4	
10-11	2	
8-9	3	
6-7	1	
	N = 50	

1. Obtain 50% of N.
   a. The total number of cases (N) of this distribution equals 50.
   b. 50%, or ½ of N equals $\dfrac{50}{2} = 25$.

2. Count up (or down) the frequency column.
   a. Starting at the bottom of the f column, $1 + 3 + 2 + 4 + 5 = 15$. The next class has 14 frequencies in it, which if added to the total of 15 would go beyond 50% of N. We therefore approximate the median to be half-way between these two classes, 14-15 and 16-17, which is 15.5.

3. Compute the correction.
   a. Subtract the cumulative frequencies, 15, from $\dfrac{N}{2}$ 25. This results in $25 - 15 = 10$, which means that we must go into the class, 16-17 for 10 more score units to find the median. There are 14 frequencies in this class which means that the median is $\dfrac{10}{14}$ of the distance in the class.
   b. The size of the class interval is 2. The correction, therefore, is $\dfrac{10}{14}$ of 2 or 1.43.

4. Obtain the median.
   a. The median (or 50th percentile) is obtained by adding the correction to the score halfway between the two classes which was 15.5 (obtained in step 2).
   b. The median of this distribution is $15.5 + 1.43 = 16.93$.
   c. The median may also be obtained by counting down the frequency column. In this instance, starting at the top of the f column, $1 + 0 + 2 + 1 + 1 + 3 + 1 + 8 + 4 = 21$.

$$17.5 - \left(\frac{25 - 21}{14} \times 2\right) = 17.5 - .57 = 16.93.$$

In addition to measures of central tendency and variability test scores may be interpreted through the use of norms or standard scores. In health education, physical education and recreation the types used most frequently are T-scores and percentiles.

Standard scores and percentiles. The T-score is a standard score and is computed from the mean and standard deviation, using the following formula:

$$T = 50 + \frac{10(X - M)}{SD}$$

where X is the symbol for the individual raw score, M is the symbol for mean and SD is standard deviation. For example, in a distribution where the mean equals 25 and the standard deviation is 4, the T-score for the raw score of 31 is computed as follows:

$$T = 50 + \frac{10(31 - 25)}{4} = 65$$

The mid-point on the T-scale is 50 and each standard deviation is equal to ten points on the T-scale. Thus, a raw score which is exactly one standard deviation above the mean would have a T-score of 60 since the mean would be 50 on the T-scale and one standard deviation above the mean would be 50 + 10.

T-scores range from approximately 20 to 80 with roughly 68% of the scores between 40 and 60. The T-scale is useful because raw scores on different tests may be easily compared by converting them into T-scores. T-scores may be totaled or averaged to provide an over-all score for a number of tests. For example:

	Test I		Test II		TOTAL
STUDENT	RAW SCORE	T-SCORE	RAW SCORE	T-SCORE	T-SCORE
S	118	62	9	68	130
A	59	21	8	65	86
Q	155	80	9	68	148

If a number of tests are combined, it may be easier to average the T-scores by totaling them and dividing by the number of tests. For example, student S would have an average T-score of $\frac{130}{2} = 65$.

Percentiles are also used in interpreting test scores. The distribution is divided into 100 parts and individuals are ranked in the group. A person who scores at the 60th percentile has done better than 60% of the other persons in the group.

The median is the 50th percentile. The 75th percentile is Q_3 and the 25th percentile is Q_1. Thus, a person who scores at Q_3 has done better than 75% of the group and at Q_1 better than 25%.

The same procedures are used for determining a score at a given percentile as were described for finding the median. For example, if the problem were to find the score at the 25th percentile of a given distribution, (a) obtain 25% of N, (b) count up the frequency column, (c) compute the correction and (d) determine the score.

To illustrate, using the same frequency distribution as for obtaining the median:

1. Obtain 25% of N.
   a. N = 50
   b. 25% of 50 = 12.5
2. Count up the frequency column.
   a. 1 + 3 + 2 + 4 = 10. The next class has 5 frequencies in it which would take us beyond 25% of N.
   b. We approximate the score to be halfway between the classes which is 13.5.
3. Compute the correction.
   a. Subtract cumulative frequencies from 25% N.

$$12.5 - 10 = 2.5$$

   b. There are 5 frequencies in the class and the size of the class interval is 2.

$$\text{Correction is } \frac{2.5}{5} \times 2 = 1$$

4. Determine the score at the 25th percentile.
   a. Score is 13.5 + correction.

$$13.5 + 1 = 14.5$$

   b. Score at 25th percentile is 14.5.

To obtain the percentile rank of each score in a distribution a cumulative frequency (cf) column is added and the following formula is used:

$$\frac{cf + \frac{1}{2}f}{N} \times 100 \qquad$$ where cf = cumulative frequencies below
the given score
N = number of cases
f = frequences at the given score

To illustrate:

Classes	f	cf		Computation
34-35	1	50		To find the percentile rank of class 34-35:
32-33	0	49		
30-31	2	49		cf = 49
28-29	1	47		f = 1
26-27	1	46		N = 50
24-25	3	45		To find the percentile rank of class 6-7:
22-23	1	42		
20-21	8	41		cf = 0
18-19	4	33		f = 1
16-17	14	29		N = 50
14-15	5	15		
12-13	4	10		
10-11	2	6		
8-9	3	4		
6-7	1	1		

$$\frac{49 + \frac{1}{2}(1)}{50} \times 100 = 99$$

$$\frac{0 + \frac{1}{2}(1)}{50} \times 100 = 1$$

Further descriptions for computing measures of central tendency, measures of variability, standard scores and percentiles may be found in the literature (5, 6, 7).

There are a few published knowledge examinations in health education and physical education which may be used instead of a teacher-constructed test if the test items cover the particular material which was taught and if the students for whom the test was constructed are similar to the students being measured.

Before a published test is used it must be carefully analyzed as to content and suitability for the particular group being measured in addition to the criteria for good test construction.

Published knowledge examinations in health education include:

Dearborn, Terry H., *College Health Knowledge Test*. Stanford, California: Stanford University Press, 1950.

Kilander, H. F., *Kilander Health Knowledge Test for College Students*. Ann Arbor, Michigan: J. W. Edwards and Sons, 1959.

Veenker, C. Harold, "A Health Knowledge Test for the Seventh Grade," *Research Quarterly*, 30: 338-348, 1959.

Published knowledge examinations in physical education include:

Scott, M. Gladys, "Achievement Examination for Elementary and Intermediate Swimming Classes," *Research Quarterly*, 11: 100, 1940.

Waglow, I. F. and C. H. Rehling, "A Golf Knowledge Test," *Research Quarterly*, 24: 463-70, 1953.

Waglow, I. F. and F. Stephens, "A Softball Knowledge Test," *Research Quarterly*, 26: 234-43, 1955.

Selected References

1. Adkins, Dorothy C., *Construction and Analysis of Achievement Tests.* Washington, D. C.: U. S. Government Printing Office, 1947.

2. American Association for Health, Physical Education, and Recreation, *Research Methods in Health, Physical Education and Recreation*, 2nd Ed. Washington, D. C.: American Association for Health, Physical Education, and Recreation, 1959.

3. Bulletin of the California State Department of Education, *Evaluating Pupil Progress, Vol. XXI, No. 6.* Sacramento: California State Department of Education, 1952.

4. Flanagan, John C., "General Considerations in the Selection of Test Items and a Short Method of Estimating the Product-Moment Coeffcient from Data at the Tails of the Distribution," *Journal of Educational Psychology*, Vol. 30, 1939, p. 674.

5. Guilford, J. P., *Fundamental Statistics in Psychology and Education*, 2nd Ed. New York: McGraw-Hill Book Company, 1950.

6. Ross, C. C. and Julian C. Stanley, *Measurement in Today's Schools*, 3rd Ed. Englewood Cliffs, N. J.: Prentice-Hall, Inc., 1954.

7. Scott, M. Gladys and Esther French, *Measurement and Evaluation in Physical Education.* Dubuque, Iowa: William C. Brown Company Publishers, 1959.

12

EVALUATION OF PROGRAMS

EVALUATION COMPETENCIES

To *understand*:
  1. how to evaluate program organization or framework
  2. how to evaluate the total program

EXPERIENCES FOR THE STUDENT

1. Using the "Check List for Appraising Program Organization" included in this chapter, evaluate a specific program.
2. Construct a check list for evaluating program organization. Include a statement of the principles or values you are using.
3. Select a published evaluation instrument (suggested in the bibliography at the end of the chapter) and evaluate a given program.
4. Discuss with administrative personnel the results of your evaluations.

School and community must provide experiences of all kinds for the education of children, youth and adults. To help the individual obtain the experiences he wants and needs, the school and community organize their experiences into programs. A program is usually focused on a specific subject matter such as physical education or on a specific objective such as helping the individual meet his leisure time needs.

A school curriculum is all of the experiences provided for the student by the school, organized into many programs—English, history, health education, mathematics. At the present time many of these programs including health education, physical education and recreation are provided both in the school and in the community. The organization of these programs determines whether or not the individual's objectives will be achieved.

Programs are, or should be, organized to help individuals learn. Principles of teaching-learning are, therefore, the bases of program organization. Program organization includes the titles and description of the experiences, the time blocks for specific experiences, rules or requirements for entrance to the program, sequence of particular experiences within the program.

Unfortunately, the program organization or structure has an aura surrounding it which causes teachers and leaders to hesitate to suggest changing it. Consequently outmoded program structure continues to successfully hamper the implementation of a methodology to meet present day needs in teaching-learning. It is difficult for a teacher to be creative or to experiment in a rigid program structure which is *only* subject matter oriented in limited time blocks. A change in program organization immediately contributes to change in the teaching-learning situation.

Teachers in health education and physical education have long been hampered by rigid, subject-matter centered programs in the schools, with inadequate time provided for helping students meet the objectives of healthy growth and development.

How to Evaluate Program Organization

The same criteria should be used to evaluate program organization as is used to evaluate teaching-learning. To illustrate this point, the criteria used in Chapter 7 for evaluating instruction are also used here to evaluate organization of program experiences.

Check List for Appraising Program Organization

PURPOSE: 1. To determine if the organization implements the stated philosophy as reflected by the accepted learning principles
2. To determine if the organization facilitates the achievement of the accepted objectives

Directions to the evaluator: Check your response to each item in the appropriate space. Under "comments" write any suggestions you have for improving the application of the particular principle.

YES   NO   I. PURPOSE: Purposes or objectives must be clearly defined so that procedures for attaining the purposes may be readily determined. Group goals or objectives must be the purposes of the individuals who comprise the group.

____   ____   1. Are program objectives derived from the needs of the individuals for whom the program is developed?

YES   NO

_____ _____   2. Are the cultural conditions of the particular environment considered in setting up objectives?

_____ _____   3. Is recent scientific information used in determining objectives?

_____ _____   4. Are objectives in agreement with the stated philosophy?

_____ _____   5. Are trends and happenings in the larger society considered in setting up objectives?

_____ _____   6. Does the program organization allow for the identification of the needs of each of the participants?

Comment:

II. EXPERIENCES: The experiences must be so closely related to the purposes that purpose and experience are inseparable. Experiences should extend the personal world of the individual.

_____ _____   7. Are specific courses problem-centered so experiences are selected to meet the purposes of the participants?

_____ _____   8. Are "course boundaries" and "time blocks" flexible to allow for exploration and creativity?

_____ _____   9. Do courses provide opportunities for individuals to do better what they are already doing?

_____ _____   10. Do courses provide opportunities for individuals to participate in new experiences?

_____ _____   11. Does program organization permit extension of experiences into the community?

Comment:

III. INDIVIDUAL DEVELOPMENT: The individual should have an opportunity to achieve his own goals irrespective of group goals.

_____ _____   12. Does program organization provide opportunity for each participant to understand his

YES   NO

own individual purposes and to achieve them?

_____ _____ 13. Are courses in the program "elective" rather than "required" to allow for individual variation in the needs of the participants?

Comment:

IV. SOCIAL DEVELOPMENT: An individual should have opportunity to participate with other individuals in achieving common goals.

_____ _____ 14. Does program organization allow for the forming of groups *following* identification of individual purposes of the participants?

_____ _____ 15. Does the program organization provide flexibility in making changes when needed?

_____ _____ 16. Does the program organization provide many opportunities for group participation?

Comment:

V. SEQUENCE: Organization and progression of experiences should proceed hand-in-hand with individual development.

_____ _____ 17. Is sequence of experiences determined by progression of subject matter skills and knowledges, growth and development levels, interests and inquiry?

_____ _____ 18. Are course prerequisites flexible to allow for different sequences to provide for individual patterns?

Comment:

VI. EVALUATION: Evaluation should be used to determine and clarify purposes and to appraise progress in goal achievement.

_____ _____ 19. Is evaluation used to help each participant in the program find out where he is in relation to where he wants and needs to be?

_____ _____   20. Is evaluation used to help each person plan
                        his own unique pattern of program experi-
                        ences?

YES   NO

_____ _____   21. Is evaluation used to appraise progress in
                        individual goal achievement in meeting pro-
                        gram objectives?

_____ _____   22. Does program organization allow for mobil-
                        ity of participants based on the results of
                        evaluation?

Comment:

The organization of programs is of major concern to teachers and leaders since it may either facilitate or block the teaching-learning situation. If we remember that the same criteria are used for evaluating organization of programs as are used for evaluating teaching-learning, we may readily recognize that changes in methodology or teaching-learning also require changes in organization. For example, a particular student learning may be desired by school or community. The program organization may prevent the learning to occur even if a new course is added to provide for the desired learning.

How to Evaluate the Total Program

Teachers and leaders may evaluate their programs by using published evaluative criteria provided by national and state agencies or by determining the values for their own particular programs as criteria against which to evaluate.

Many professional organizations have specialists in evaluation who form an evaluation committee to offer service to those wishing it. Teachers and leaders can write to their national and state education associations and professional organizations for assistance. These same groups publish evaluation materials to be used by teachers and leaders in self study, or an evaluation team may be provided on request to appraise the program. Some of these materials which can be used and should be purchased and studied by teachers and leaders are described here.

The 1960 edition of "Evaluative Criteria" (10) covers the evaluation of most subjects in the public schools plus the student activity program, library, guidance services, health services, school plant, school staff and administration. The entire list of sections may be obtained or individual sections may be ordered if so desired. The section for health education is D-9, for physical education (boys), D-14 and (girls), D-15, guidance services, G, and health services, H. The checklists include organization of the program, nature of offerings, physical facilities, instructional staff, instructional activities, instructional materials and equipment and methods of evaluation.

"Guide to a Community Health Study," 1960 edition (5) is a well-prepared evaluation tool for assessing community resources, maternal and child health, health of school-age children, health of the adult, control of infections, environmental health and community mental health. It is recommended that the guide be used as a whole in order to obtain a clear picture of needs and problems in the community. Directions for using the guide are included in the publication.

"Evaluation Schedules" in recreation, in physical education and in health education may be obtained from the national association (1, 2, 3). These schedules are for the purpose of evaluating college and university programs in these fields. They include criteria for selection and retention of students, placement and follow-up services, recruitment, preparation of undergraduate and graduate faculty, evaluation of curriculum and instructional patterns, evaluation of library and evaluation of facilities and equipment.

Materials for evaluating the elementary school physical education program, grades kindergarten through six, may be obtained from the California State Department of Education (4). Check lists and evaluation tools are frequently published by state departments of education for the purpose of evaluating school programs (6, 11, 12, 13).

The National Recreation Association provides check lists for evaluating community recreation (8, 9) and a revision of the 1954 National Conference Report of the American Association for Health, Physical Education, and Recreation (7) provides principles which may be used as guides in planning and evaluating the physical education program for college men and women.

Teachers and leaders who wish to determine their own criteria for evaluating their programs must first describe the program as it *should* be for the school or agency at *that particular time* in *that particular community*. The program as it should be may be called the *ideal state of affairs* or the *ideal program*. The ideal program is the program which is most practical, which is right for the participants in the particular area at this time.

The ideal program is best developed by the participants, teachers and leaders, with the assistance of trained consultants who are curriculum specialists. The present program may then be evaluated against the ideal program and problem areas may then be identified.

Determination of values against which to appraise the program may follow these steps:

1. State the philosophy which is to be implemented

2. Derive the purposes or objectives from (a) the trends or happenings in society and (b) the nature of the individual and characteristics of his healthy growth and development

3. Determine which objectives are achieved by the *way* you teach and which are achieved by *what* you teach and describe experiences for meeting these objectives

4. Determine organization and sequence of experiences from the philosophy, the nature of the individual and his purposes, individual growth and development and subject matter progressions.

Procedures may be determined which put these values into operation. These implementing procedures may be set up in check list form and the program may be appraised against the ideal for the particular situation.

Selected References

1. American Association for Health, Physical Education and Recreation, *Evaluation Schedules in Health Education*. Washington 6, D.C.: American Association for Health, Physical Education, and Recreation.

2. ———, *Evaluation Schedules in Physical Education*. Washington 6, D.C.: American Association for Health, Physical Education and Recreation.

3. ———, *Evaluation Schedules in Recreation*. Washington 6, D.C.: American Association for Health, Physical Education and Recreation.

4. California State Department of Education, *Criteria for Evaluating the Physical Education Program: Kindergarten, Grades One Through Six*. Sacramento: State Department of Education, 1960.

5. Committee on Public Health Administration of the American Public Health Association, *Guide To A Community Health Study*. New York: American Public Health Association, 1960.

6. Elliott, Eugene B. (Superintendent of Public Instruction), *A Checklist for Surveying the Secondary School Health Program*. Lansing, Michigan: State Department of Public Instruction, 1954.

7. National Conference Report of the American Association for Health, Physical Education, and Recreation, *Physical Education for College Men and Women, Revised*. Washington 6, D.C.: American Association for Health, Physical Education, and Recreation, 1959.

8. National Recreation Association, *Schedule for the Appraisal of Community Recreation, Rev. Ed.* New York: National Recreation Association, 1951.

9. ――――, *Know Your Community*. New York: National Recreation Association.

10. National Study of Secondary School Evaluation, *Evaluative Criteria*. Washington 6, D.C.: National Education Association, 1960.

11. Texas Education Agency, A Checklist: *Appraising the Elementary and Secondary Health Programs, Bulletin 519*. Austin, Texas: Texas Education Agency, April, 1951.

12. The Ohio Association for Health, Physical Education, and Recreation, *Evaluative Criteria for Physical Education*. Columbus, Ohio: State Department of Education.

13. University of the State of New York, *Evaluation of School Health Education*. Albany, New York: The State Education Department, December, 1952.

INDEX

INDEX

A

Activities, physical education:
  evaluation of, 191-94
Activity skills, physical education:
  assessment of, 190ff.
  how to assess, 197ff.
Adkins, Dorothy C., 247
Allport, Gordon, 17, 147
Amer. Assoc. for Health, Phys. Ed. and
      Recreation, 189, 215, 247,
      253, 254
American Medical Assoc., 22, 129
American Public Health Assoc., 254
Anderson, Gladys L., 147
Anderson, Harold H., 17, 147, 156,
  160, 169, 189
Anecdotal record, 107, 127ff.
  construction of, 127-28
Anthropometric measures (*see also*
      Body size and proportions):
  discussion of, 42-43
Aquatics, 190 (*see also* Movement
      skills)
Archery tests, 211
Ashton, Dudley, 213
Assoc. for Supervision and Curriculum
      Development, 14, 17, 179
Athletic Institute, The, 186
Attitude, appraisal of, 143-44
  compared to interests, 139
  definition of, 143
Attitude inventory, 130, 154
  construction of, 145-46
  for assessing motives, 143ff.
  scoring and interpretation of, 146
Ausubel, David P., 17
Autobiography, description of, 29ff.
  as assessment of status, 42
  of movement, 29-31

B

Badminton tests, 212
Barrow, Harold, 105
Baseball tests, 212

Basketball tests, 212
Behavior:
  coping, 107, 117
  democratic, 161-65
  expressive, 107
Bennet, LaVerne Means, 213
Bernard, Harold W., 139, 143, 147
Bloom, Benjamin, 178
Body size and proportions, discussion
      of, 41ff.
  as measure of status, 41
  height, how to measure, 43, 52
  weight, how to measure, 52
Borleske, Stanley E., 213
Bowling tests, 212
Brace, David K., 105
Brace Test, 66
Brady, George F., 215
Bresnahan, George T., 189
Broer, Marion R., 214
Brown, Camille, 170
Buchanan, Ruth E., 214
Bulletin of the Calif. State Dept. of
      Ed., 105, 147, 215, 247
Bulletin of the Dept. of Elementary
      School Principals, 110, 129
Bunn, John W., 215
Burdg, Barbara, 113, 120

C

Calif. State Dept. of Ed., 155, 156,
      253, 254
  Bulletin of, 105, 147, 215, 247
Cassidy, Rosalind, 9, 147, 170
Central tendency (*see* Statistics)
Check list, 150, 154
  construction of, 195-97
  for appraising programs, 248
  for assessing form in movement skills,
      195-97
  for evaluating total performance in
      an activity, 190
  for observation of health status, 33-
      34
Chinning, 60

259